SO-ARD-723

Buckle Down!®

on Algebra I

Book 2

This book belongs to: _____

Helping the schoolhouse meet the
standards of the statehouse™

Buckle Down
PUBLISHING COMPANY

ISBN 0-7836-2612-6

Catalog #BD US10A2 1

4 5 6 7 8 9 10

President and Publisher: Douglas J. Paul, Ph.D.; Editorial Director: John Hansen; Project Editor: Michael J. Morony; Editors: Todd Hamer, Paul Meyers; Production Editor: Michael Hankes; Production Director: Jennifer Booth; Production Supervisor: Ginny York; Art Director: Chris Wolf; Graphic Designer: Diane Hudachek.

Copyright © 2002 by Buckle Down Publishing Company. All rights reserved. No part of this work may be reproduced or transmitted in any form or by any means, electronic or mechanical, including photocopying, recording, or any information storage or retrieval systems, except as may be expressly permitted in writing by the publisher, Buckle Down Publishing Company, P.O. Box 2180, Iowa City, IA 52244-2180.

Cover image: © Corbis

TABLE OF CONTENTS

Introduction 1

    Test-Taking Tips 3

Unit 1 – Analytical Thinking 5

    Lesson 1: Polynomials 6

    Lesson 2: Factoring 34

    Lesson 3: Rational Expressions 58

    Lesson 4: Patterns 74

    Lesson 5: Matrices 102

Unit 2 – Data and Probability 113

    Lesson 6: Statistics 114

    Lesson 7: Displaying Data 121

    Lesson 8: Probability 152

Appendix 169

    Buckle Down Learning Standards and Skills
      for Algebra I, Book 2 170

© 2002 Buckle Down Publishing Company. DO NOT DUPLICATE.

Introduction

If you are reading this book, you probably have some compelling reasons to be studying algebra. Let us venture a guess about one of those reasons: You have an important algebra test in the near future.

Maybe you have to pass this test to pass your course, get your credits, graduate from high school, eventually get into college, and, way down the road, get that job you've always dreamed of as a . . . well, what *do* you want to be? If you're thinking you might like to be a rocket scientist, a stockbroker, a computer game designer, the head park ranger at a national forest, an airline pilot, a restaurant owner, a sports writer (think of all those statistics!) or any of a thousand and one other jobs, then—you guessed it—you'll need some algebra skills to succeed. Of course, whether you need to know a little algebra or a lot will depend on the job.

More than likely, you're not too sure about what you want to be doing in ten years. You're probably far more concerned about that test coming up in ten days, or ten weeks, or ten months. And that's probably for the best. We're just trying to give you some extra encouragement by assuring you that all the algebra you're learning now may help you in the future—long after your next test—in ways you can't even imagine yet. We've said it before, but that's why schools require you to learn algebra: you'll need it.

© 2002 Buckle Down Publishing Company. DO NOT DUPLICATE.

About this Book

Buckle Down on Algebra I, Book 2, is designed to help you develop your algebra skills, no matter what your needs or goals might be. In this book, you will review advanced algebra topics and skills, including polynomials, factoring, rational expressions, patterns, matrices, and data and probability. Many of the problems you will solve in this book use algebra to represent everyday math problems, as well as problems from other subject areas, such as science and social studies.

Buckle Down on Algebra I, Book 1, reviews the foundations of algebra, from the nature of numbers through basic operations with integers, fractions, and decimals. The main focus of the book is on reviewing the concepts and skills needed to solve equations and inequalities in one and two variables.

If you work through all the activities in these books, you should be very well prepared for any algebra test you might take. For example, your state may require you to take an end-of-course Algebra I test to get a diploma. If you plan to attend college, you will need to take either the SAT or ACT. The *Buckle Down on Algebra I* books may help you to answer many of the algebra questions on those college entrance exams.

Before you begin with Lesson 1, read the test-taking tips that follow.

© 2002 Buckle Down Publishing Company. DO NOT DUPLICATE.

Test-Taking Tips

Here are a few general tips to keep in mind on test day.

Tip 1: On test day, take it easy.

If you've practiced the material in this book, your new algebra skills will be "built in" by test day. Worry drifts away when you know you're prepared. A little nervousness is natural and may actually help you stay aware and focused. Take a few deep breaths and tell yourself something good before you dive into the test.

Tip 2: Remember to have all your supplies.

Make sure you have at least a couple of sharpened No. 2 pencils and an eraser with you on test day. Your teacher will tell you if you need anything else.

Tip 3: Pace yourself.

You will have plenty of time to take the test, but it's up to you to make sure you use the time wisely. If you take a quick flip through the test, you can get a good sense of which items you will solve quickly and which items will require more time. There is no rule that says you have to start at item one. This technique will help you get "grounded" in the test and help you set your own pace. On a second flip through the test, attack the items that require less time, then go back to the items that require more time. Take a final flip to see if you've left any blanks. If you did, write something down—do not leave any items blank.

Tip 4: Answer all multiple-choice items.

Most of the items on the test will be multiple choice. Every item has an answer and a way to solve it. But if your answer doesn't match any of the choices after a few attempts, you may need to guess. Sometimes, the wrong answers will be more obvious than the right answer, so eliminate any unreasonable choices. Usually, you can get the number of choices down to two. If you are totally stumped, just pick an answer. The probability of getting a correct answer by guessing is 25%, which is better than 0%, the probability of getting a correct answer if you leave it blank.

© 2002 Buckle Down Publishing Company. DO NOT DUPLICATE.

Tip 5: Answer open-ended items completely.

Open-ended items require that you show your work to receive maximum credit. Sometimes, there is more than one method for solving an item. Pick an appropriate method, show the work, and make sure your solution is correct. There is no need to show more than one way to arrive at the solution; it could count against you if a human scorer can't follow what needs to be scored. Also, clearly indicate your answer(s) by circling them, drawing arrows to them, or using your own device.

Tip 6: Keep a sense of humor and perspective.

Make a commitment to do the best you can to prepare for any algebra test. The time to be concerned about whether you know the algebra is now, not a week before the test. As you review all the lessons in this book and solve all the "Practice" and "Test Your Skills" items, keep your sense of humor. Sure, you'll miss a few problems. Big deal. The purpose of this workbook is to find the areas that you need to improve, and then develop the knowledge and skills you need to approach the material with confidence. Other students have used this book to succeed, and you will, too.

Tip 7: Change your approach to algebra.

Some students tell themselves, "I am never going to need this," or, "I don't have a mathematical mind." Neither statement is true. Instead of telling yourself that you *never, don't, can't, won't* when you speak about algebra, do this: remove those words from your vocabulary. Look for your strengths rather than reinforcing what you think you can't or won't do. You definitely have more math talent than you realize. It's a matter of allowing yourself to believe it.

© 2002 Buckle Down Publishing Company. DO NOT DUPLICATE.

Unit 1

Analytical Thinking

Many people throughout the world use analytical thinking along with algebra techniques to solve different types of problems. For example, a building contractor can use polynomials to determine how much the area of a room will increase by building an addition onto the room. An office worker can use sequences to determine what her salary will be in 5 years with the same company if she receives an annual raise of 5%.

In this unit, you will compute with polynomials, factor binomials and trinomials, and simplify and compute rational expressions. You will find rules for and extend number patterns. You will find the nth term of a sequence and find the sum of the first n terms of a series. Predictions and decisions will be made based on observations of sequences. You will also add and subtract matrices, as well as multiply matrices by a scalar.

In This Unit

Polynomials

Factoring

Rational Expressions

Patterns

Matrices

© 2002 Buckle Down Publishing Company. DO NOT DUPLICATE.

Lesson 1: Polynomials

This lesson reviews polynomials and computing with polynomials. It also reviews the rules for exponents.

Monomials

A **monomial** is a constant, a variable, or the product of one or more constants and one or more variables.

Adding or subtracting monomials

When adding or subtracting monomials, they must be **like terms**. Like terms have the same variables, each raised to the same power.

$3a^4b$ and $-5a^4b$ are like terms. $4x^7yz^5$ and $2x^5yz^7$ are not like terms.

To add or subtract like terms, add or subtract the coefficients while leaving the bases and exponents as they are.

Example

Add: $8a^3b^2 + (-5a^3b^2)$

These are like terms, so add the coefficients and leave the bases and the exponents as they are.

$$8a^3b^2 + (-5a^3b^2) = \left[8 + (-5)\right]a^3b^2 = 3a^3b^2$$

Therefore, $8a^3b^2 + (-5a^3b^2) = 3a^3b^2$.

Example

Subtract: $-6xy^4z^2 - xy^4z^2$

Again, these are like terms, so subtract the coefficients (the second term has a coefficient of 1 that is not written) and leave the bases and the exponents as they are.

$$-6xy^4z^2 - xy^4z^2 = (-6 - 1)xy^4z^2 = -7xy^4z^2$$

Therefore, $-6xy^4z^2 - xy^4z^2 = -7xy^4z^2$.

© 2002 Buckle Down Publishing Company. DO NOT DUPLICATE.

Practice

Directions: For Numbers 1 through 8, add or subtract the monomials.

1. $-5x^3y^2 + (-9x^3y^2)$

2. $7u^7v^5 - (-3u^7v^5)$

3. $13j^2k^9l - j^2k^9l$

4. $-3z^{12} + 3z^{12}$

5. $-8x^5y^5 + (-5x^5y^5)$

6. $7x^2z^3 - 2y^2z^3$

7. $6a^3b^9c - (-4a^3b^9c)$

8. $-r^7s^2t^3 + (-2r^7s^2t^3)$

© 2002 Buckle Down Publishing Company. DO NOT DUPLICATE.

Multiplying monomials

When multiplying monomials, multiply the coefficients and add the exponents of the like bases (variables).

Example

Multiply: $(x^7)(x^{12})$

Remember that both terms have a coefficient of 1 that is not written.

$$(x^7)(x^{12}) = (1 \cdot 1)(x^{7+12}) = x^{19}$$

Therefore, $(x^7)(x^{12}) = x^{19}$.

Example

Multiply: $(-3x^4)(2x)$

Remember that the exponent of the x in $2x$ is 1.

$$(-3x^4)(2x) = (-3 \cdot 2)(x^{4+1}) = -6x^5$$

Therefore, $(-3x^4)(2x) = -6x^5$.

In the next two examples, there is more than one variable in each term. Add the exponents of each variable independently.

Example

Multiply: $(-4x^5y^2)(x^8y^7)$

$$(-4x^5y^2)(x^8y^7) = (-4 \cdot 1)(x^{5+8})(y^{2+7}) = -4x^{13}y^9$$

Therefore, $(-4x^5y^2)(x^8y^7) = -4x^{13}y^9$.

Example

Multiply: $(-12a^3b^2c)(a^7b^5d^4)$

$$(-12a^3b^2c)(a^7b^5d^4) = (-12 \cdot 1)(a^{3+7})(b^{2+5})(c^1)(d^4) = -12a^{10}b^7cd^4$$

Therefore, $(-12a^3b^2c)(a^7b^5d^4) = -12a^{10}b^7cd^4$.

© 2002 Buckle Down Publishing Company. DO NOT DUPLICATE.

Practice

Directions: For Numbers 1 through 8, multiply the monomials.

1. $(3x^3y^2)(-6xy^7)$

2. $(-a^6b^7)(-3b^7c^5)$

3. $(16g^4h^3i^8)(3ghi)$

4. $(-3x^7y^2z^9)(4z^2)$

5. $(-a^4b^2c^8)(a^4b^2c^8)$

6. $(4a^2b^3)(9x^4y^2z^7)$

7. $(5a^3b^7c^9)(-5ab^2c^3d)$

8. $(-8f^7g^3h)(2f^2g^9h^2)$

© 2002 Buckle Down Publishing Company. DO NOT DUPLICATE.

Dividing monomials

When dividing monomials, reduce the coefficients (write them in lowest terms) and subtract the exponents (larger − smaller) of the like bases (variables). Put the base and its new exponent in the numerator or denominator, wherever the larger exponent originally was. (In the examples below, the bases with the larger exponents are shown in bold-faced type.)

Example

Divide: $\dfrac{9a^4\boldsymbol{b^7}c}{12a^4b^4\boldsymbol{c^3}}$

Remember, if you don't see an exponent on a variable, then the exponent is a 1.

$$\frac{9a^4\boldsymbol{b^7}c}{12a^4b^4\boldsymbol{c^3}} = \frac{9}{12} \bullet \frac{a^{4-4}b^{7-4}}{c^{3-1}} = \frac{3b^3}{4c^2}$$

Therefore, $\dfrac{9a^4\boldsymbol{b^7}c}{12a^4b^4\boldsymbol{c^3}} = \dfrac{3b^3}{4c^2}$.

If all the bases with the higher exponents are in the numerator or denominator, write a 1 where the bases with the lower exponents were.

Example

Divide: $\dfrac{2a^4b^2}{6\boldsymbol{a^6}\boldsymbol{b^3}}$

$$\frac{2a^4b^2}{6\boldsymbol{a^6}\boldsymbol{b^3}} = \frac{2}{6} \bullet \frac{1}{a^{6-4}b^{3-2}} = \frac{1}{3a^2b}$$

Therefore, $\dfrac{2a^4b^2}{6\boldsymbol{a^6}\boldsymbol{b^3}} = \dfrac{1}{3a^2b}$.

Example

Divide: $\dfrac{8\boldsymbol{x^4}\boldsymbol{y^5}\boldsymbol{z^3}}{2x^2y^4}$

$$\frac{8\boldsymbol{x^4}\boldsymbol{y^5}\boldsymbol{z^3}}{2x^2y^4} = \frac{8}{2} \bullet \frac{x^{4-2}y^{5-4}z^3}{1} = \frac{4x^2yz^3}{1} = 4x^2yz^3$$

Therefore, $\dfrac{8\boldsymbol{x^4}\boldsymbol{y^5}\boldsymbol{z^3}}{2x^2y^4} = 4x^2yz^3$.

© 2002 Buckle Down Publishing Company. DO NOT DUPLICATE.

Practice

Directions: For Numbers 1 through 8, divide the monomials.

1. $\dfrac{x^5 y^2}{x^3 y^7}$

2. $\dfrac{4a^3 b^2 c}{14ab^5 c^2}$

3. $\dfrac{-5x^2 y^3 z}{-6y^5 z^3}$

4. $\dfrac{8a^4 b^2}{-12a^4 b^2}$

5. $\dfrac{12x^4 y^3}{15x^4 y^7 z^3}$

6. $\dfrac{-17a^3 b^2 c^5 d}{34a^2 b^5 c^5 d^3}$

7. $\dfrac{27a^4 b^3 c}{18a^2 b^8 c^3}$

8. $\dfrac{-f^7 g^4 h^2}{-5f^8 g^2 h^4}$

© 2002 Buckle Down Publishing Company. DO NOT DUPLICATE.

Monomials raised to a power

When raising a monomial to a power, raise the coefficient to the power and multiply each exponent by the power.

Example

Simplify: $(j^6k^2l^3)^4$

Remember, when you raise a 1 to any power, it equals 1.

$$(j^6k^2l^3)^4 = 1^4(j^{6 \bullet 4})(k^{2 \bullet 4})(l^{3 \bullet 4}) = j^{24}k^8l^{12}$$

Therefore, $(j^6k^2l^3)^4 = j^{24}k^8l^{12}$.

Example

Simplify: $(-7ab^5)^2$

Remember, if you don't see an exponent on a variable, it is a 1.

$$(-7ab^5)^2 = (-7)^2(a^{1 \bullet 2})(b^{5 \bullet 2}) = 49a^2b^{10}$$

Therefore, $(-7ab^5)^2 = 49a^2b^{10}$.

Any negative coefficient raised to an even power is positive. Any negative coefficient raised to an odd power is negative.

Example

Simplify: $(-3x^2y^5)^4$

$$(-3x^2y^5)^4 = (-3)^4(x^{2 \bullet 4})(y^{5 \bullet 4}) = 81x^8y^{20}$$

Therefore, $(-3x^2y^5)^4 = 81x^8y^{20}$.

Example

Simplify: $(-4d^2e^3)^5$

$$(-4d^2e^3)^5 = (-4)^5(d^{2 \bullet 5})(e^{3 \bullet 5}) = -1{,}024d^{10}e^{15}$$

Therefore, $(-4d^2e^3)^5 = -1{,}024d^{10}e^{15}$.

© 2002 Buckle Down Publishing Company. DO NOT DUPLICATE.

Practice

Directions: For Numbers 1 through 8, simplify each monomial raised to a power.

1. $(6a^4g^2)^3$

2. $(-5x^4y)^6$

3. $(-9f^7g^5h^4)^3$

4. $(-7w)^4$

5. $(8x^5y^7z^6)^4$

6. $\left(\frac{1}{3}v^5w^8\right)^4$

7. $(r^7s^2t)^6$

8. $\left(-\frac{2}{5}j^2k^6l^3\right)^4$

© 2002 Buckle Down Publishing Company. DO NOT DUPLICATE.

Monomials with negative exponents

When simplifying a monomial with a negative exponent, the monomial equals its reciprocal with a positive exponent.

$$x^{-5} = \frac{1}{x^5} \qquad \text{and} \qquad \frac{1}{x^{-3}} = x^3$$

Example

Simplify: 7^{-3}

$$7^{-3} = \frac{1}{7^3} = \frac{1}{343}$$

Therefore, $7^{-3} = \frac{1}{343}$.

When simplifying a monomial with variables that have negative exponents, rewrite the monomial using only positive exponents on the variables.

Example

Simplify: $4x^2y^{-6}z^{-8}$

$$4x^2y^{-6}z^{-8} = (4)(x^2)(y^{-6})(z^{-8}) = (4)(x^2)\left(\frac{1}{y^6}\right)\left(\frac{1}{z^8}\right) = \frac{4x^2}{y^6z^8}$$

Therefore, $4x^2y^{-6}z^{-8} = \frac{4x^2}{y^6z^8}$.

The previous monomial rules for adding, subtracting, multiplying, dividing, and raising to a power still hold for monomials with negative exponents. Be sure to rewrite the answers so that they do not include any negative exponents.

Example

Multiply: $(4a^3b^{-5}c^{-1})(-5a^{-6}b^{-1}c)$

$$(4a^3b^{-1})(-5a^{-6}b) = [4 \bullet (-5)][a^{3 + (-6)}](b^{-1 + 1}) = -20a^{-3} = -\frac{20}{a^3}$$

Therefore, $(4a^3b^{-5}c^{-1})(-5a^{-6}b^{-1}c) = -\frac{20}{a^3}$.

Example

Simplify: $(3x^2y^{-4})^{-4}$

$$(3x^2y^{-4})^{-4} = 3^{-4}[x^{2 \bullet (-4)}][y^{-4 \bullet (-4)}] = \frac{1}{81}x^{-8}y^{16} = \frac{y^{16}}{81x^8}$$

Therefore, $(3x^2y^{-4})^{-4} = \frac{y^{16}}{81x^8}$.

© 2002 Buckle Down Publishing Company. DO NOT DUPLICATE.

Practice

Directions: For Numbers 1 through 8, simplify, multiply, or divide. Be sure your answers do not include any negative exponents.

1. $(3^{-5})(3^9)$

2. $[(-4)^{-3}][(-4)^{-5}]$

3. $4a^{-3}b^5c^{-6}de^{-1}$

4. $(3h^2j^{-5}k^{-3})(-6h^4j^{-3}k^7)$

5. $(-8x^{-4}y^2z^{-9})(-x^7y^2z^{-3})$

6. $\dfrac{9a^7b^{-4}c^{-9}d^{-1}}{-3a^{-7}b^3c^{-3}}$

7. $(6m^{-4}n^7)^{-5}$

8. $(-4w^{-3}x^5y^{-7}z^3)^3$

© 2002 Buckle Down Publishing Company. DO NOT DUPLICATE.

Square roots

A perfect square monomial has a perfect square coefficient and even exponents on every variable. The monomials $4x^2$, $16b^6$, and $25m^{12}$ are perfect squares.

To simplify the square root ($\sqrt{}$) of a monomial, find the square root of the coefficient (recall from Lesson 1 of Book 1) and divide the exponent(s) of the variable(s) by 2. Remember that each perfect square has two roots, one positive and one negative. Perfect square monomials will also have two roots. Use the principal (positive) root when stating your answer.

Example

Simplify: $\sqrt{16x^6y^2}$

How do you know that this monomial is a perfect square? Its coefficient, 16, is a perfect square. In addition, the exponents on every variable are even.

$$\sqrt{16x^6y^2} = \sqrt{4^2 x^{(2\,\bullet\,3)} y^{(2\,\bullet\,1)}} = 4x^3y$$

Therefore, $\sqrt{16x^6y^2} = 4x^3y$.

Example

Simplify: $\sqrt{w^4 x^8 y^{12} z^6}$

The coefficient is a 1, which is a perfect square with a square root of 1.

$$\sqrt{w^4 x^8 y^{12} z^6} = \sqrt{1^2 w^{(2\,\bullet\,2)} x^{(2\,\bullet\,4)} y^{(2\,\bullet\,6)} z^{(2\,\bullet\,3)}} = w^2 x^4 y^6 z^3$$

Therefore, $\sqrt{w^4 x^8 y^{12} z^6} = w^2 x^4 y^6 z^3$.

Example

Simplify: $\sqrt{\frac{4}{9} a^4 b^6}$

The coefficient in this example is a fraction. A fraction is a perfect square if both the numerator and denominator are perfect squares. In this case, $\frac{4}{9}$ is a perfect square since both 4 and 9 are perfect squares.

$$\sqrt{\frac{4}{9} a^4 b^6} = \sqrt{\left(\frac{2}{3}\right)^2 a^{(2\,\bullet\,2)} b^{(2\,\bullet\,3)}} = \frac{2}{3} a^2 b^3$$

Therefore, $\sqrt{\frac{4}{9} a^4 b^6} = \frac{2}{3} a^2 b^3$.

© 2002 Buckle Down Publishing Company. DO NOT DUPLICATE.

Practice

Directions: For Numbers 1 through 8, write the principal square root of each monomial.

1. $\sqrt{a^2 b^{10} c^8}$

2. $\sqrt{64x^8}$

3. $\sqrt{0.16 r^6 s^4 t^{16}}$

4. $\sqrt{121 x^{14} y^{26} z^4}$

5. $\sqrt{100 j^8 k^{18}}$

6. $\sqrt{\frac{1}{4} z^6}$

7. $\sqrt{49 f^6 g^8 h^2}$

8. $\sqrt{\frac{25}{81} a^2 b^{10}}$

© 2002 Buckle Down Publishing Company. DO NOT DUPLICATE.

Cube roots

A perfect cube monomial has a perfect cube coefficient and exponents that are multiples of three on every variable. Here are some perfect cubes.

$$\ldots, -64, -27, -8, -1, 0, 1, 8, 27, 64, \ldots$$

To find the cube root $\left(\sqrt[3]{}\right)$ of a monomial, find the cube root of the coefficient and divide the exponent(s) of the variable(s) by 3.

Example

Simplify: $\sqrt[3]{216x^9y^3z^{27}}$

How do you know this monomial is a perfect cube? Its coefficient, 216, is a perfect cube. In addition, all of its exponents are multiples of 3.

$$\sqrt[3]{216x^9y^3z^{27}} = \sqrt[3]{6^3x^{(3 \cdot 3)}y^{(3 \cdot 1)}z^{(3 \cdot 9)}} = 6x^3yz^9$$

Therefore, $\sqrt[3]{216x^9y^3z^{27}} = 6x^3yz^9$.

Sometimes a perfect cube coefficient is negative. In this case, the cube root will also be negative.

Example

Simplify: $\sqrt[3]{-27a^{12}b^{36}}$

Again, the coefficient, –27, is a perfect cube (its cube root is also negative), and all exponents are multiples of three.

$$\sqrt[3]{-27a^{12}b^{36}} = \sqrt[3]{(-3)^3a^{(3 \cdot 4)}b^{(3 \cdot 12)}} = -3a^4b^{12}$$

Therefore, $\sqrt[3]{-27a^{12}b^{36}} = -3a^4b^{12}$.

 TIP: You can find the real cube root of a negative real number but the real square root of a negative real number does not exist.

© 2002 Buckle Down Publishing Company. DO NOT DUPLICATE.

© 2002 Buckle Down Publishing Company. DO NOT DUPLICATE.

Practice

Directions: For Numbers 1 through 8, write the cube root of each monomial.

1. $\sqrt[3]{a^9 b^{15} c^{21}}$

2. $\sqrt[3]{-8a^3 b^9 c^3 d^{24}}$

3. $\sqrt[3]{0.000064 x^6 y^3}$

4. $\sqrt[3]{-343 x^{18} y^6}$

5. $\sqrt[3]{1{,}000 f^6 g^9 h^{30}}$

6. $\sqrt[3]{\dfrac{8}{27} a^9 b^{24} c^9}$

7. $\sqrt[3]{125 x^9 y^{12} z^3}$

8. $\sqrt[3]{-216 j^6 k^6 l^{15}}$

Polynomials

A **polynomial** is a monomial or the sum of monomials. Each monomial of a polynomial is called a **term** of the polynomial. A polynomial with two terms is called a **binomial**. A polynomial with three terms is called a **trinomial**. The terms of a polynomial are usually written in **standard form:** decreasing order of the exponents of the variable or of one of the variables. The **degree of a term** of a polynomial is the sum of each exponent of each variable of that term. The **degree of the polynomial** is the highest degree of the individual terms of that polynomial. For example, the degrees of the terms of $4x^3y^2 + 2x^2y^4 - xy^8$ are 5, 6, and 9. The degree of the polynomial is 9.

Adding polynomials

To add polynomials, add the like terms of the polynomials.

 Example

Add: $(4x^3 + 7x^2 - 5x) + (-9x^2 + 6x)$

The like terms are the x^2- and x-terms. There is only one x^3-term, so it will stay the same.

$$(4x^3 + 7x^2 - 5x) + (-9x^2 + 6x) = 4x^3 + [7 + (-9)]x^2 + (-5 + 6)x$$

$$= 4x^3 - 2x^2 + x$$

Therefore, $(4x^3 + 7x^2 - 5x) + (-9x^2 + 6x) = 4x^3 - 2x^2 + x$.

Subtracting polynomials

To subtract polynomials, add the opposite. Change the $-$ to $+$ and every term in the second polynomial to its opposite, then follow the rule for addition.

 Example

Subtract: $(x - 6) - (4x^2 - 7x + 5)$

Change $-$ to $+$ and change each term of $4x^2 - 7x + 5$ to its opposite. Then add.

$$(x - 6) - (4x^2 - 7x + 5) = (x - 6) + (\mathbf{-4x^2 + 7x - 5})$$

$$= -4x^2 + 8x - 11$$

Therefore, $(x - 6) - (4x^2 - 7x + 5) = -4x^2 + 8x - 11$.

© 2002 Buckle Down Publishing Company. DO NOT DUPLICATE.

Adding and subtracting polynomials using algebra tiles

Some algebraic procedures might be easier to understand when you apply geometric concepts to create a model for the problem. These algebra tiles represent algebraic expressions and real numbers. Shaded tiles indicate negative algebraic expressions and real numbers. Algebraic tiles can be used to show addition and subtraction of polynomials.

This tile is 1 unit by 1 unit. The tile represents 1:

$$\boxed{1}$$

This tile is 1 unit by x units. The tile represents x:

$$\boxed{x}$$

This tile is x units by x units. The tile represents x^2:

$$\boxed{x^2}$$

This tile is 1 unit by 1 unit. The tile represents -1:

$$\boxed{-1}$$

This tile is 1 unit by x units. The tile represents $-x$:

$$\boxed{-x}$$

This tile is x units by x units. The tile represents $-x^2$:

© 2002 Buckle Down Publishing Company. DO NOT DUPLICATE.

Addition

Combine the like terms. Remember that opposite terms add to zero.

Example

Add: $(2x^2 + 3x - 4) + (x^2 - 5x + 2)$

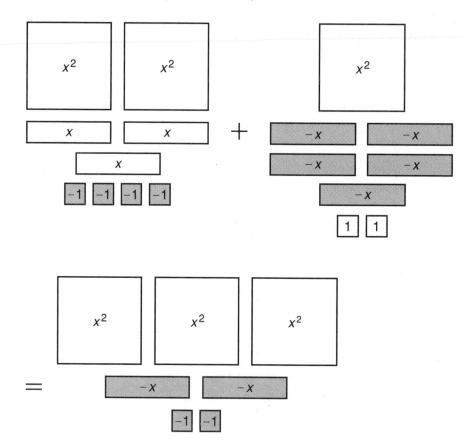

Therefore, $(2x^2 + 3x - 4) + (x^2 - 5x + 2) = 3x^2 - 2x - 2$.

© 2002 Buckle Down Publishing Company. DO NOT DUPLICATE.

Subtraction

Add the opposite. Change − to + and each term of the second polynomial to its opposite. Then add.

⬩∴⬩ Example

Subtract: $(3x^2 + 4x - 5) - (2x^2 - x - 2)$

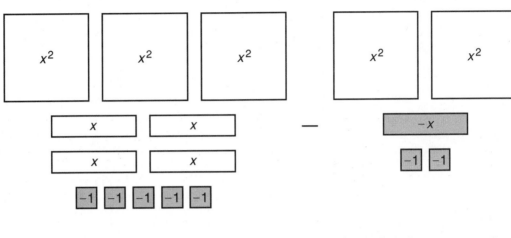

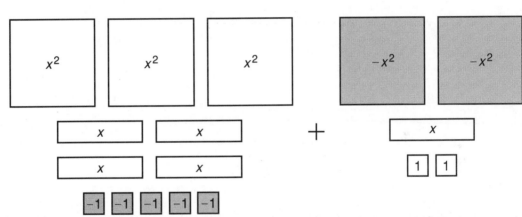

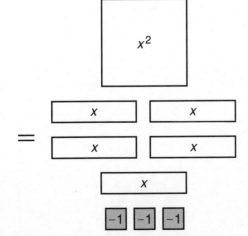

Therefore, $(3x^2 + 4x - 5) - (2x^2 - x - 2) = x^2 + 5x - 3$.

© 2002 Buckle Down Publishing Company. DO NOT DUPLICATE.

Practice

Directions: For Numbers 1 through 8, add or subtract the polynomials.

1. $(6x^2y - 4xy^2) + (-9x^2y - 7xy^2)$

2. $(6x^2y - 4xy^2) - (-9x^2y - 7xy^2)$

3. $(5y^3 + 8y^2 - 6) + (9y^3 - 2y^2 + 3y)$

4. $(5y^3 + 8y^2 - 6) - (9y^3 - 2y^2 + 3y)$

5. $(-8x^2 - 7xy + 5y^2) + (-5x^2 - 6xy + y^2)$

6. $(-8x^2 - 7xy + 5y^2) - (-5x^2 - 6xy + y^2)$

7. $(4x^4 + 3x^3y - 5xy^3) + (-7x^4 - 9x^2y^2 + y^4)$

8. $(4x^4 + 3x^3y - 5xy^3) - (-7x^4 - 9x^2y^2 + y^4)$

© 2002 Buckle Down Publishing Company. DO NOT DUPLICATE.

Multiplying polynomials

To multiply polynomials, use a form of the distributive property. Multiply each term of the first polynomial by each term of the second polynomial, then combine the like terms when appropriate. When multiplying two binomials, you can use the acronym FOIL (First, Outer, Inner, Last) to help you remember what terms to multiply.

Example

Multiply: $5w(7w^2 - 8w + 3)$

Multiply $5w$ by each term of $7w^2 - 8w + 3$. Follow the rules for multiplying monomials.

$$5w(7w^2 - 8w + 3) = (5w \cdot 7w^2) - (5w \cdot 8w) + (5w \cdot 3)$$

$$= 35w^3 - 40w^2 + 15w$$

Therefore, $5w(7w^2 - 8w + 3) = 35w^3 - 40w^2 + 15w$.

Example

Multiply: $(3x + 4)(4x^2 - 6x + 2)$

Multiply $3x$ by each term of $4x^2 - 6x + 2$. Then multiply 4 by each term of $4x^2 - 6x + 2$. Finally, combine the like terms.

$$(3x + 4)(4x^2 - 6x + 2) = 12x^3 - 18x^2 + 6x + 16x^2 - 24x + 8$$

$$= 12x^3 - 2x^2 - 18x + 8$$

Therefore, $(3x + 4)(4x^2 - 6x + 2) = 12x^3 - 2x^2 - 18x + 8$.

Example

Multiply: $(x - 5)(2x + 3)$

Use the acronym FOIL to multiply the binomials.

$$(x - 5)(2x + 3) = 2x^2 + 3x - 10x - 15$$

$$= 2x^2 - 7x - 15$$

Therefore, $(x - 5)(2x + 3) = 2x^2 - 7x - 15$.

© 2002 Buckle Down Publishing Company. DO NOT DUPLICATE.

Dividing polynomials

To divide polynomials, use a process similar to long division of real numbers. As with place value in real numbers, make sure you keep the terms lined up.

Example

Divide: $(6x^3 - 2x^2 + 8x) \div 2x$

Set up the division similar to long division of a three-digit real number by a one-digit real number.

$$
\begin{array}{r}
3x^2 - x + 4 \\
2x\overline{\smash{)}6x^3 - 2x^2 + 8x} \\
\underline{- (6x^3)} \downarrow \\
-2x^2 \\
\underline{- (-2x^2)} \downarrow \\
8x \\
\underline{- 8x} \\
0
\end{array}
$$

Therefore, $(6x^3 - 2x^2 + 8x) \div 2x = 3x^2 - x + 4$.

Example

Divide: $(2x^2 + x - 15) \div (x + 3)$

Set it up as a long division problem.

$$
\begin{array}{r}
2x - 5 \\
x + 3\overline{\smash{)}2x^2 + x - 15} \\
\underline{- (2x^2 + 6x)} \downarrow \\
-5x - 15 \\
\underline{- (-5x - 15)} \\
0
\end{array}
$$

Therefore, $(2x^2 + x - 15) \div (x + 3) = 2x - 5$.

© 2002 Buckle Down Publishing Company. DO NOT DUPLICATE.

Multiplying and dividing polynomials using algebra tiles

Algebraic tiles can also be used to show multiplication and division of some polynomials. Multiplication must be between two monomials, two binomials, or a monomial and a binomial. Each must have at most one variable, and each variable must have a greatest degree of 1 (the greatest exponent on any term is 1). Division must be a trinomial divided by a binomial, a binomial divided by either a binomial or a monomial, or a monomial divided by a monomial, each with at most one variable. The polynomial being divided (the dividend) can be of at most degree 2. The polynomial doing the dividing can be of at most degree 1.

Multiplication

Multiplication can be shown as the area of a rectangular array of tiles. The sides of the rectangle have lengths that correspond to each factor.

Example

Multiply: $(3x - 1)(x - 3)$

Create a rectangle whose side lengths represent $3x - 1$ and $x - 3$.

Divide the rectangle into smaller sections by drawing in partitions for each value of $\pm x$ and ± 1. Label each of these sections by multiplying the dimensions of the section (shade where necessary). Then combine the like terms to find the product.

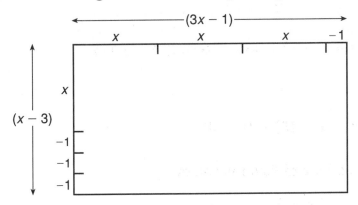

Therefore, $(3x - 1)(x - 3) = 3x^2 - 10x + 3$.

© 2002 Buckle Down Publishing Company. DO NOT DUPLICATE.

Division

Because division is the opposite of multiplication, it can also be shown using a rectangular array of tiles. Use the divisor as the length of one side of the rectangle. Then finish the rectangle to correspond to the dividend. The quotient will be the other dimension of the array.

Example

Divide: $(2x^2 - 5x - 12) \div (2x + 3)$

Draw the top of a rectangle with a side length of $2x + 3$.

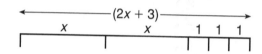

Now create the rest of a rectangle that represents the dividend, $2x^2 - 5x - 12$. In order to get sections that total $2x^2$, draw a row of width x. The row also makes sections that total $3x$. Since the middle term of the dividend is $-5x$ and the x-length along the top is positive, rows of length -1 are needed to make $-x$ sections. Each row of length -1 makes sections that total $-2x$ and -3. Four rows of length -1 make sections that total $-8x$ and -12. The $-8x$ sections combined with the $3x$ sections from the top row make $-5x$. The last term of the dividend, -12, is already accounted for.

The polynomial that corresponds to the width of the rectangle is $x - 4$.

Therefore, $(2x^2 - 5x - 12) \div (2x + 3) = x - 4$.

© 2002 Buckle Down Publishing Company. DO NOT DUPLICATE.

Practice

Directions: For Numbers 1 through 8, multiply or divide the polynomials.

1. $(3x - 6)(2x + 9)$

2. $(4x^3 - 6x^2 + 12x) \div 2x$

3. $(3y^3 + 11y^2 - 25y - 25) \div (y + 5)$

4. $(3x^2 - 5)(x^3 + 6x^2 - 8x + 3)$

5. $4x^2y^3(6x^2 - 5xy + y^2)$

6. $(3x^3 - 7x^2 + 11x - 3) \div (x^2 - 2x + 3)$

7. $(4x - 3)(5x^2 + 7x)$

8. $(3x^4 - 7x^3 - 9x^2 + 41x - 20) \div (3x^2 + 5x - 4)$

© 2002 Buckle Down Publishing Company. DO NOT DUPLICATE.

Applications with Polynomials

You may use computation with polynomials in problem-solving situations. In some cases, it may be helpful to use diagrams similar to the algebra tiles.

Example

The floor of John's garage was square. He then built an addition onto the garage. The addition added 4 ft to the length of the garage and 5 feet to the width of the garage. What is the area of the garage with the addition?

The dimensions of the garage are not given, but the garage was square. Therefore, label each of the original dimensions x. Add the dimensions of the addition to the garage.

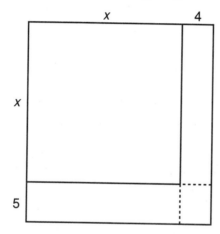

Multiply to find the area of each section of the garage with the addition.

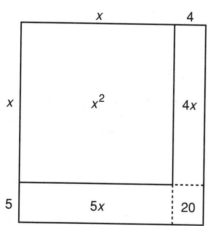

Find the area of the garage with the addition by adding the areas of the sections.

$$x^2 + 4x + 5x + 20 = x^2 + 9x + 20$$

The area of the garage with the addition is $x^2 + 9x + 20$.

© 2002 Buckle Down Publishing Company. DO NOT DUPLICATE.

Practice

1. Bob wants to add on to his workout room. It is now 15 ft by 18 ft. He is going to add on the same length (x) to both dimensions, but doesn't know by how much. What is the amount of floor space that Bob will **add** to his workout room?

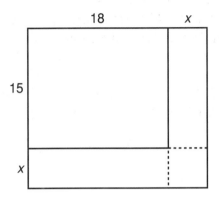

2. Louise has a rectangular pool in her backyard. The length of the pool is 3 times the width of the pool. All the way around the pool there is a pool deck that is twice the width of the pool and 12 ft more than the length of the pool. What is the area of the pool deck?

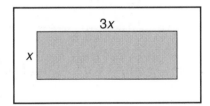

3. Jack, Jeremy, and Jimmy are brothers. Jack is x years old. Jeremy is eight years less than 3 times as old as Jack. Jimmy is 2 times as old as Jeremy. What polynomials represent the ages of Jeremy and Jimmy? What is the polynomial that represents the combined ages of the brothers?

© 2002 Buckle Down Publishing Company. DO NOT DUPLICATE.

Test Your Skills

1. Simplify:

$$\frac{8x^4y^2z^3}{(-4x^2y^3z)(6x^4y^5)}$$

   A. $-\dfrac{z^2}{3x^2y^6}$

   B. $-\dfrac{x^2z^2}{3y^6}$

   C. $-3x^2y^6z^2$

   D. $-\dfrac{x^2z^2}{16y^6}$

2. Divide:

$$\frac{-16x^4y^5z^2}{32x^8yz^2}$$

   A. $-2x^4y^4$

   B. $-\dfrac{y^4z}{2x^4}$

   C. $-\dfrac{y^5z}{2x^2}$

   D. $-\dfrac{y^4}{2x^4}$

3. Simplify:

$$\sqrt[3]{-125x^6y^9z^{12}}$$

   A. $5x^3y^6z^9$
   B. $-5x^3y^6z^9$
   C. $-5x^2y^3z^4$
   D. $5x^2y^3z^4$

4. Subtract:

$$(3x^2 + 4x + 6) - (-x^2 + 5x + 7)$$

   A. $4x^2 - x - 1$
   B. $-4x^2 + x + 1$
   C. $2x^2 + 9x + 13$
   D. $-4x - 9x - 13$

5. Multiply:

$$(3x + 6)(x^2 - 5x + 9)$$

   A. $3x^3 + 6x^2 + x + 54$
   B. $3x^3 - 9x^2 + 15x + 3$
   C. $3x^3 + 6x^2 + 9x + 15$
   D. $3x^3 - 9x^2 - 3x + 54$

6. In the space provided below, divide the following polynomials. Be sure to show your work.

$$(6x^2 - x - 35) \div (3x + 7)$$

© 2002 Buckle Down Publishing Company. DO NOT DUPLICATE.

7. Simplify:

$$4(2x^2 + 3x - 5) + 2x(3x - 6)$$

A. $14x^2 - 20$
B. $8x^2 + 18x - 8$
C. $8x^2 + 18x - 32$
D. $14x^2 + 12x - 32$

8. Simplify:

$$(-4m^4n^2)^3$$

A. $-12m^{12}n^6$
B. $-12m^7n^5$
C. $-64m^{12}n^6$
D. $-64m^7n^5$

9. Simplify:

$$\sqrt{36x^4y^6z^2}$$

A. $18x^2y^4$
B. $18x^2y^3z$
C. $6x^2y^4$
D. $6x^2y^3z$

10. Multiply:

$$(4x^2y)(-3x^4y^5)$$

A. $-12x^6y^5$
B. $-12x^6y^6$
C. $-12x^8y^5$
D. $-12x^8y^6$

11. Add:

$$(4x^2 + 4y^2) + (6y^2 - 8x^2)$$

A. $-2x^2 - 4y^2$
B. $10x^2 + 4y^2$
C. $-4x^2 + 10y^2$
D. $12x^2 - 10y^2$

12. Subtract:

$$7a^2b^{-4} - 9a^2b^{-4}$$

A. $\dfrac{16a}{b}$

B. $-\dfrac{2a^2}{b^4}$

C. $2a^2b^4$

D. $-16a^2b^4$

13. In the space provided below, simplify the following monomial raised to a power. Be sure your answer does not contain any negative exponents.

$$(3x^{-2}y^4z^{-3})^4$$

© 2002 Buckle Down Publishing Company. DO NOT DUPLICATE.

Lesson 2: Factoring

In this lesson, you will review the processes for factoring binomials and trinomials.

Greatest Common Factor (GCF)

A **factor** of a real number is any real number that divides the real number evenly (with no remainder).

 Example

Write the factors of 8, 12, and 37.

factors of 8: 1, 2, 4, and 8

factors of 12: 1, 2, 3, 4, 6, and 12

factors of 37: 1 and 37

The **greatest common factor (GCF)** of two or more real numbers is the greatest real number that divides each of the real numbers evenly.

 Example

Find the GCF of 18 and 24.

You need to find the greatest number that divides both 12 and 18 evenly. List the factors of each and choose the greatest number that appears in both lists.

factors of 18: 1, 2, 3, **6**, 9, and 18

factors of 24: 1, 2, 3, 4, **6**, 8, 12, and 24

The GCF of 18 and 24 is 6.

Another way to find the GCF is to guess and check. Find any common factor of the numbers and divide. Then look at the quotients and see if you can find another common factor. If you do, divide again and check for more common factors until there are none. Finally, multiply all the common factors that you've divided by.

$18 \div 3 = 6$ $6 \div 2 = 3$

$24 \div 3 = 8$ $8 \div 2 = 4$ GCF: $3 \cdot 2 = 6$

The GCF of 18 and 24 is 6.

© 2002 Buckle Down Publishing Company. DO NOT DUPLICATE.

You can also find the GCF of two or more monomials. To do so, find the GCF of the coefficients of each monomial. Then find the variable(s) that are common to each monomial. If there are any variables that are common, use the smallest exponent that the variable is raised to in the monomials.

Example

Find the GCF of $15x^2y^4z^5$ and $20xy^7$.

The GCF of 15 and 20 is 5.

Notice that both x and y are common to both monomials (z is found only in $15x^2y^4z^5$). The smallest exponent on x is 1 and the smallest exponent on y is 4. So, xy^4 is common to both monomials.

The GCF of $15x^2y^4z^5$ and $20xy^7$ is $5xy^4$.

Remember that 1 is a common factor of every real number and every monomial.

Practice

Directions: For Numbers 1 through 8, write the GCF for each.

1. 21, 49

   GCF: _____

2. 4, 32

   GCF: _____

3. 6, 9, 18

   GCF: _____

4. 3, 5, 8

   GCF: _____

5. $6x^2y^3z^7$, $8x^5y^2z^7$

   GCF: _____

6. ab^3c^5d, $3a^4b^2c$

   GCF: _____

7. $4a^2$, $2a$, 6

   GCF: _____

8. $9x^4$, $12x^3$, $18x^2$

   GCF: _____

© 2002 Buckle Down Publishing Company. DO NOT DUPLICATE.

Factoring the GCF from a polynomial

The first step in any factoring process is to factor the GCF from the terms of the polynomial. Factoring the GCF from a polynomial is the inverse (opposite) of multiplying using the distributive property. To factor the GCF from a polynomial, follow these steps:

Step 1: **Find the GCF of the terms of the polynomial.** (Don't worry about the signs of the terms.)

Step 2: **Divide each term of the polynomial by the GCF.** (Recall division of monomials from Lesson 1.)

Step 3: **Write your answer as the product of the GCF and the new terms of the polynomial from Step 2.**

Example

Factor the GCF from $3x^2 + 6x - 9$.

The GCF of $3x^2$, $6x$, and 9 is 3.

Divide $3x^2$, $6x$, and -9 each by 3.

$$\frac{3x^2}{3} = x^2 \qquad \frac{6x}{3} = 2x \qquad \frac{-9}{3} = -3$$

Write your answer as the product of 3 and $x^2 + 2x - 3$.

$$3x^2 + 6x - 9 = \mathbf{3(x^2 + 2x - 3)}$$

Example

Factor the GCF from $20x^3y - 45xy^3$.

The GCF of $20x^3y$ and $45xy^3$ is $5xy$.

Divide both $20x^3y$ and $-45xy^3$ by $5xy$.

$$\frac{20x^3y}{5xy} = 4x^2 \qquad \frac{-45xy^3}{5xy} = -9y^2$$

Write your answer as the product of $5xy$ and $4x^2 - 9y^2$.

$$20x^3y - 45xy^3 = \mathbf{5xy(4x^2 - 9y^2)}$$

© 2002 Buckle Down Publishing Company. DO NOT DUPLICATE.

Practice

Directions: For Numbers 1 through 8, factor the GCF from each polynomial.

1. $4x^2 + 28x + 48$

2. $2x^2 - 32$

3. $x^3 - 4x^2 - 21x$

4. $50x^3 - 72xy^2$

5. $24x^2y + 28xy - 20y$

6. $6x^4 + 18x^3 - 108x^2$

7. $9x^3y - 9xy^3$

8. $14x^3 - 63x^2y - 35xy^2$

© 2002 Buckle Down Publishing Company. DO NOT DUPLICATE.

Factoring Trinomials in the Form $x^2 \pm bx \pm c$

If a trinomial in the form $x^2 \pm bx \pm c$ is factorable, it will factor into the product of two binomials. By the symmetric property of equality, the order in which you write the binomials does not matter. Factoring a trinomial is the inverse of the FOIL process. Since the first term of each trinomial is x^2, the first term of each binomial will be x (because $x \bullet x = x^2$).

Factoring where c is positive ($x^2 \pm bx + c$)

To factor a trinomial in the form $x^2 \pm bx + c$, follow these steps:

Step 1: **Find two numbers whose product is c and whose sum is $|b|$.**

Step 2: **The signs of the binomials will be the same, they will each be the sign of the middle term of the trinomial.** (Since the signs of the binomials are the same, it won't matter which of the two numbers goes in which binomial.)

Example

Factor: $x^2 + 8x + 12$

Notice that $c = 12$ and $|b| = 8$. Find two numbers whose product is 12 and whose sum is 8. List the factor pairs of 12.

$$1 \bullet 12 = 12 \qquad 2 \bullet 6 = 12 \qquad 3 \bullet 4 = 12$$

The factor pair of 12 with a sum of 8 is 2 and 6.

Since the sign on the middle term of the trinomial $x^2 + 8x + 12$ is $+$, the signs of both binomials will be $+$.

Write the trinomial equal to the product of two binomials whose first terms are x and whose second terms are 2 and 6.

$$x^2 + 8x + 12 = (x + 2)(x + 6) \qquad [\text{or } (x + 6)(x + 2)]$$

Check your answer by using the FOIL process.

$$(x + 2)(x + 6) = x^2 + 6x + 2x + 12$$
$$= x^2 + 8x + 12 \checkmark$$

TIP: If you can't find two numbers whose product is c and whose sum is $|b|$, then the trinomial cannot be factored into two binomials.

© 2002 Buckle Down Publishing Company. DO NOT DUPLICATE.

Example

Factor: $x^2 - 16x + 15$

Notice that $c = 15$ and $|b| = 16$. Find two numbers whose product is 15 and whose sum is 16. List the factor pairs of 15.

$$1 \cdot 15 = 15 \qquad 3 \cdot 5 = 15$$

The factor pair of 15 with a sum of 16 is 1 and 15.

Since the sign on the middle term of the trinomial $x^2 - 16x + 15$ is $-$, the signs of the binomials will both be $-$.

Write the trinomial equal to the product of two binomials whose first terms are x and whose second terms are 1 and 15.

$$x^2 - 16x + 15 = (x - 1)(x - 15)$$

Check your answer by using the FOIL process.

$$(x - 1)(x - 15) = x^2 - 15x - x + 15$$
$$= x^2 - 16x + 15 \ ✔$$

Practice

Directions: For Numbers 1 through 8, factor each trinomial.

1. $x^2 + 18x + 32$

2. $x^2 - 4x + 4$

3. $x^2 - 7x + 6$

4. $x^2 + 12x + 20$

5. $x^2 + 10x + 25$

6. $x^2 - 10x + 21$

7. $x^2 + 12x + 27$

8. $x^2 - 29x + 28$

© 2002 Buckle Down Publishing Company. DO NOT DUPLICATE.

Factoring where c is negative ($x^2 \pm bx - c$)

To factor a trinomial in the form $x^2 \pm bx - c$, follow these steps:

Step 1: **Find two numbers whose product is $|c|$ and whose difference is $|b|$.**

Step 2: **The signs of the binomials will be different (one +, one −).**

Step 3: **The larger of the two numbers goes with the sign of the middle term of the trinomial.**

Example

Factor: $x^2 + 7x - 18$

Notice that $|c| = 18$ and $|b| = 7$. Find two numbers whose product is 18 and whose difference is 7. List the factor pairs of 18.

$1 \cdot 18 = 18 \qquad 2 \cdot 9 = 18 \qquad 3 \cdot 6 = 18$

The factor pair of 18 with a difference of 7 is 2 and 9.

Since the sign on the middle term of the trinomial $x^2 + 7x - 18$ is +, the 9 will go in the binomial with the + and the 2 will go with the −.

Write the trinomial equal to the product of two binomials whose first terms are x and whose second terms are 2 and 9.

$x^2 + 7x - 18 = (x - 2)(x + 9)$

Check your answer by using the FOIL process.

$(x - 2)(x + 9) = x^2 + 9x - 2x - 18$
$$= x^2 + 7x - 18 \; ✔$$

TIP: If you can't find two numbers whose product is $|c|$ and whose difference is $|b|$, then the trinomial cannot be factored into two binomials.

© 2002 Buckle Down Publishing Company. DO NOT DUPLICATE.

Example

Factor: $x^2 - 9x - 10$

Notice that $|c| = 10$ and $|b| = 9$. Find two numbers whose product is 10 and whose difference is 9. List the factor pairs of 10.

$$1 \bullet 10 = 10 \qquad 2 \bullet 5 = 10$$

The factor pair of 10 with a difference of 9 is 1 and 10.

Since the sign on the middle term of the trinomial $x^2 - 9x - 10$ is $-$, the 10 will go in the binomial with the $-$ and the 1 will go with the $+$.

Write the trinomial equal to the product of two binomials whose first terms are x and whose second terms are 1 and 10.

$$x^2 - 9x - 10 = (\boldsymbol{x + 1})(\boldsymbol{x - 10})$$

Check your answer by using the FOIL process.

$$(x + 1)(x - 10) = x^2 - 10x + x - 10$$
$$= x^2 - 9x - 10 \; \checkmark$$

Practice

Directions: For Numbers 1 through 8, factor each trinomial.

1. $x^2 + 12x - 13$

2. $x^2 - 2x - 35$

3. $x^2 - 2x - 3$

4. $x^2 + x - 6$

5. $x^2 + 2x - 63$

6. $x^2 - 44x - 45$

7. $x^2 + 15x - 34$

8. $x^2 - 47x - 48$

© 2002 Buckle Down Publishing Company. DO NOT DUPLICATE.

Factoring Trinomials in the Form $ax^2 \pm bx \pm c$

If it is factorable, a trinomial in the form $ax^2 \pm bx \pm c$, where $a > 1$, will factor into the product of two binomials. The order in which you write the binomials does not matter. This type of trinomial factoring is a little more involved and will use some of the ideas of both GCF factoring and factoring trinomials in the form $x^2 \pm bx \pm c$. To factor a trinomial in the form $ax^2 \pm bx \pm c$, follow these steps:

Step 1: **Find the product of a and $|c|$.**

Step 2: **Find two numbers whose product is the same as the product from Step 1 and whose sum or difference is $|b|$, depending on whether c is positive (sum) or negative (difference).** If no two numbers like this exist, the trinomial cannot be factored into two binomials.

Step 3: **Rewrite the middle term of the trinomial as two terms using the factor pair from Step 2 as the coefficients.** If c is positive, the signs on the factor pair will be the same, whichever the sign of the middle term of the trinomial is. If c is negative, the signs on the factor pair will be different with the larger number of the factor pair having the same sign as the sign of the middle term of the trinomial.

Step 4: **Group the first two terms and the last two terms of the new polynomial from Step 3 and factor the GCF from each.**

Step 5: **Write your answer as the product of the common binomial and the binomial formed by the GCFs from Step 4.**

© 2002 Buckle Down Publishing Company. DO NOT DUPLICATE.

Example

Factor: $8x^2 - 19x + 6$

Find the product of a and $|c|$. ($a = 8$ and $c = 6$)

$8 \cdot 6 = 48$

Find two numbers whose product is 48 and whose sum (since c is positive) is 19. List the factor pairs of 48.

$1 \cdot 48 = 48 \qquad 2 \cdot 24 = 48 \qquad 3 \cdot 16 = 48$

$4 \cdot 12 = 48 \qquad 6 \cdot 8 = 48$

The factor pair of 48 with a sum of 19 is 3 and 16.

Rewrite the middle term ($-19x$) of the trinomial using the 3 and 16 as coefficients. Since c is positive and the sign on the middle term is $-$, the signs on $3x$ and $16x$ will be the same: they'll both be $-$.

$8x^2 - 19x + 6 = 8x^2 - 3x - 16x + 6$

Group the first two terms ($8x^2$ and $-3x$) and the last two terms ($-16x$ and 6) of the new polynomial.

$(8x^2 - 3x) + (-16x + 6)$

Factor the GCF from each grouping. The GCF of $8x^2$ and $-3x$ is x, and the GCF of $-16x$ and 6 is -2. (Use -2 to keep the first term of the group positive after you factor the GCF.)

$8x^2 - 3x = x(8x - 3) \qquad -16x + 6 = -2(8x - 3)$

Notice that the binomial within the ( ) in both cases is the same. That is the common binomial. The other binomial in your answer will be formed from the GCFs of the two groupings ($x - 2$).

$8x^2 - 19x + 6 = \mathbf{(8x - 3)(x - 2)} \quad$ [or $\mathbf{(x - 2)(8x - 3)}$]

Check your answer by using the FOIL process.

$(8x - 3)(x - 2) = 8x^2 - 16x - 3x + 6$

$= 8x^2 - 19x + 6 \; ✔$

Example

Factor: $5x^2 - 23x - 10$

Find the product of a and $|c|$. ($a = 5$ and $c = 10$)

    $5 \bullet 10 = 50$

Find two numbers whose product is 50 and whose difference (since c is negative) is 23. List the factor pairs of 50.

    $1 \bullet 50 = 50$ $2 \bullet 25 = 50$ $5 \bullet 10 = 50$

The factor pair of 50 with a difference of 23 is 2 and 25.

Rewrite the middle term ($-23x$) of the trinomial using 2 and 25 as coefficients. Since c is negative and the sign on the middle term is $-$, the signs on $2x$ and $25x$ will be different and $25x$ will have the same sign as the middle term of the trinomial ($-$).

    $5x^2 - 23x - 10 = 5x^2 - 25x + 2x - 10$

Group the first two terms ($5x^2$ and $-25x$) and the last two terms ($2x$ and -10) of the new polynomial.

    $(5x^2 - 25x) + (2x - 10)$

Factor the GCF from each grouping. The GCF of $5x^2$ and $-25x$ is $5x$, and the GCF of $2x$ and -10 is 2.

    $5x^2 - 25x = 5x(x - 5)$ $2x - 10 = 2(x - 5)$

Notice that the binomial within the ( ) in both cases is the same. That is the common binomial. The other binomial in your answer will be formed from the GCFs of the two groupings ($5x + 2$).

    $5x^2 - 23x - 25 = \boldsymbol{(x - 5)(5x + 2)}$

Check your answer by using the FOIL process.

    $(x - 5)(5x + 2) = 5x^2 + 2x - 25x - 10$

                     $= 5x^2 - 23x - 10$ ✔

© 2002 Buckle Down Publishing Company. DO NOT DUPLICATE.

Practice

Directions: For Numbers 1 through 8, factor each trinomial.

1. $6x^2 - 5x - 4$

2. $2x^2 + 21x + 27$

3. $10x^2 - 39x + 14$

4. $4x^2 + 3x - 27$

5. $3x^2 + 17x + 10$

6. $12x^2 - 8x - 15$

7. $5x^2 + 4x - 9$

8. $9x^2 - 6x + 1$

© 2002 Buckle Down Publishing Company. DO NOT DUPLICATE.

Factoring Binomials in the form $a^2 - c^2$

Binomials in the form $a^2 - c^2$ are called the "difference of two squares." Notice that both terms of the binomial are perfect squares and they are separated by $-$. Recall from Lesson 1 that perfect square monomials have perfect square coefficients and even exponents on every variable. Binomials in this form will factor into the product of two binomials. The order in which you write the binomials does not matter. To factor a binomial in the form $a^2 - c^2$, follow this formula:

$$a^2 - c^2 = (a + c)(a - c)$$

Example

Factor: $x^2 - 25$

Be sure both terms of the binomial are perfect squares.

x^2: coefficient is 1, a perfect square; exponent is even

25: a perfect square

Find the square roots of each term. (Recall Lesson 1.)

$$\sqrt{x^2} = x \qquad \sqrt{25} = 5$$

Substitute the square roots of the terms in the formula.

$$x^2 - 25 = (x + 5)(x - 5) \quad [\text{or } (x - 5)(x + 5)]$$

Check your answer by using the FOIL process.

$$(x + 5)(x - 5) = x^2 - 5x + 5x - 25$$
$$= x^2 - 25 \ ✔$$

TIP: Binomials that are not in the form $a^2 - c^2$ cannot be factored into two binomials.

© 2002 Buckle Down Publishing Company. DO NOT DUPLICATE.

Factor: $9x^2 - 49y^4$

Be sure both terms of the binomial are perfect squares.

$9x^2$: coefficient is 9, a perfect square; exponent is even

$49y^4$: coefficient is 49, a perfect square; exponent is even

Find the square roots of each term. (Recall Lesson 1.)

$$\sqrt{9x^2} = 3x \qquad \sqrt{49y^4} = 7y^2$$

Substitute the square roots of the terms in the formula.

$$9x^2 - 49y^4 = (\mathbf{3x + 7y^2})(\mathbf{3x - 7y^2})$$

Check your answer by using the FOIL process.

$$(3x + 7y^2)(3x - 7y^2) = 9x^2 - 21xy^2 + 21xy^2 - 49y^4$$
$$= 9x^2 - 49y^4 \ \checkmark$$

Practice

Directions: For Numbers 1 through 8, factor each binomial.

1. $x^2 - 4$

2. $16x^2 - 1$

3. $25x^2 - 81$

4. $4x^2 - 121$

5. $x^2 - 100y^6$

6. $36x^2 - 169$

7. $16x^2 - 9$

8. $144x^2 - y^8$

© 2002 Buckle Down Publishing Company. DO NOT DUPLICATE.

Completely Factoring Polynomials

You've reviewed the individual processes for factoring polynomials of different types in this lesson. When you factor, always see if you can factor a GCF from the polynomial first. Then try to factor any remaining binomial or trinomial according to its type. Check all polynomials in your answer to see if they can be factored again. There may be some polynomials that can be factored a number of different times. Be sure all factors are included in your final answer. The order in which you write the binomials does not matter.

 Example

Factor: $2x^4 - 4x^3 - 70x^2$

Check for a GCF. The GCF of $2x^4$, $4x^3$, and $70x^2$ is $2x^2$. Factor $2x^2$ from the trinomial.

$$2x^4 - 4x^3 - 70x^2 = 2x^2(x^2 - 2x - 35)$$

Don't assume you're done at this point. Check to see if you can factor the resulting trinomial $(x^2 - 2x - 35)$.

Recall factoring a trinomial in the form $x^2 - bx - c$.

$$x^2 - 2x - 35 = (x + 5)(x - 7) \quad [\text{or } (x - 7)(x + 5)]$$

Check to see if you can factor $x + 5$ and/or $x - 7$ again. Neither can be factored again (they do not fit the "difference of two squares" form).

Be sure to go back and find all the different factors that have been factored from the original polynomial for your final answer.

$$2x^4 - 4x^3 - 70x^2 = 2x^2(x^2 - 2x - 35)$$
$$= \mathbf{2x^2(x + 5)(x - 7)} \quad [\text{or } \mathbf{2x^2(x - 7)(x + 5)}]$$

Check your answer by multiplying using the distributive property and/or the FOIL process. Remember you can only multiply two polynomials at one time.

$$2x^2(x + 5)(x - 7) = (2x^3 + 10x^2)(x - 7)$$
$$= 2x^4 - 14x^3 + 10x^3 - 70x^2$$
$$= 2x^4 - 4x^3 - 70x^2 \checkmark$$

© 2002 Buckle Down Publishing Company. DO NOT DUPLICATE.

Example

Factor: $16x^4 - 81$

Check for a GCF. The GCF of $16x^4$ and 81 is 1. Factoring by 1 doesn't change the binomial. Continue with the other factoring processes.

Check and see if you can factor the binomial. The binomial is in the form of the "difference of two squares." Factor accordingly.

$$16x^4 - 81 = (4x^2 + 9)(4x^2 - 9)$$

Check to see if you can factor $4x^2 + 9$ and/or $4x^2 - 9$ again. You cannot factor $4x^2 + 9$ again, but you can factor $4x^2 - 9$ again: it also is in the "difference of two squares" form.

$$4x^2 - 9 = (2x + 3)(2x - 3)$$

Check to see if you can factor $2x + 3$ and/or $2x - 3$ again. Neither can be factored again.

Find all the different factors that have been factored from the original polynomial for your final answer.

$$16x^4 - 81 = (4x^2 + 9)(4x^2 - 9)$$
$$\mathbf{= (4x^2 + 9)(2x + 3)(2x - 3)}$$

Check your answer by multiplying using the distributive property and/or the FOIL process.

$$(4x^2 + 9)(2x + 3)(2x - 3) = (8x^3 + 12x^2 + 18x + 27)(2x - 3)$$
$$= 16x^4 - 24x^3 + 24x^3 - 36x^2 + 36x^2$$
$$- 54x + 54x - 81$$
$$= 16x^4 - 81 \ \checkmark$$

© 2002 Buckle Down Publishing Company. DO NOT DUPLICATE.

Directions: For Numbers 1 through 8, completely factor each polynomial.

1. $24x^2 + 6x - 30$

2. $81x^4 - 625$

3. $4x^4 - 12x^3 - 112x^2$

4. $8x^3 + 14x^2 + 3x$

© 2002 Buckle Down Publishing Company. DO NOT DUPLICATE.

5. $128x^3 - 98x$

6. $15x^2y - 93xy + 18y$

7. $12x^2 - 13x - 14$

8. $48x^5y - 3xy^3$

© 2002 Buckle Down Publishing Company. DO NOT DUPLICATE.

Using Factoring to Solve Quadratic Equations

You can find the zeros (solutions) of any quadratic function (or equation) using the quadratic formula. The zeros of some quadratic equations can also be found using factoring. The key thing to remember is that any time you multiply two or more numbers and your product is 0, at least one of the numbers must be zero (zero-product property). To solve any quadratic equation, follow these steps:

Step 1: **Set the quadratic equal to zero.** Get all terms on the same side of the equal sign.

Step 2: **Completely factor the quadratic expression.**

Step 3: **Set any factor that contains a variable equal to zero and solve for the variable.**

Step 4: **Check your solutions by substituting each of them for x in the original equation.**

Example

Solve: $6x^2 + 3x = 45$

Set the quadratic expression equal to zero by subtracting 45 from both sides.

$$6x^2 + 3x = 45$$
$$6x^2 + 3x - 45 = 0$$

Completely factor the quadratic expression.

$$6x^2 + 3x - 45 = 0$$
$$3(2x^2 + x - 15) = 0$$
$$3(2x - 5)(x + 3) = 0$$

According to the zero-product property, at least one of 3, $2x - 5$, or $x + 3$ must be zero. Since 3 is a constant, it cannot be zero. So either $2x - 5$ or $x + 3$ must be zero. Set each equal to zero and solve for x.

$$2x - 5 = 0 \qquad \text{or} \qquad x + 3 = 0$$

$$2x = 5 \qquad\qquad\qquad x = -3$$

$$x = \frac{5}{2}$$

© 2002 Buckle Down Publishing Company. DO NOT DUPLICATE.

Check your solutions.

$$6x^2 + 3x = 45 \qquad \text{or} \qquad 6x^2 + 3x = 45$$

$$6\left(\frac{5}{2}\right)^2 + 3\left(\frac{5}{2}\right) = 45 \qquad\qquad 6(-3)^2 + 3(-3) = 45$$

$$6\left(\frac{25}{4}\right) + 3\left(\frac{5}{2}\right) = 45 \qquad\qquad 6(9) + 3(-3) = 45$$

$$\frac{75}{2} + \frac{15}{2} = 45 \qquad\qquad 54 - 9 = 45$$

$$45 = 45 \;\checkmark \qquad\qquad 45 = 45 \;\checkmark$$

The solutions of $6x^2 + 3x = 45$ are $x = \frac{5}{2}$ and $x = -3$.

Practice

Directions: For Numbers 1 through 8, solve each quadratic equation. Be sure to check your solutions.

1. $x^2 - 3x - 28 = 0$

2. $245x^2 = 125$

3. $x^2 + 88 = 19x$

© 2002 Buckle Down Publishing Company. DO NOT DUPLICATE.

4. $12x^2 - 20x + 4 = 6x + 14$

5. $66 - 403x^2 = 12 - 19x^2$

6. $40x^2 - 18x - 38 = 4x^2 + 3x - 8$

7. $217x^2 + 15 = 18 - 26x^2$

8. $6x^2 + 7x + 9 = 5x + 12 - 2x^2$

© 2002 Buckle Down Publishing Company. DO NOT DUPLICATE.

Applications with Factoring

You may use factoring to solve quadratic equations in problem-solving situations. At the end of Lesson 1 (pages 30 and 31), you solved some application problems with polynomials. You will now use those polynomial solutions to find numerical solutions to the same problems. This can be done using factoring and the zero-product property.

Example

Recall John and his garage from page 30. The area of the garage with the addition is represented by the trinomial $x^2 + 9x + 20$. If the area of the garage is now 600 ft^2, what are the dimensions of the garage?

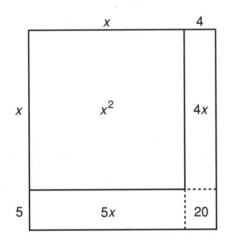

Since $x^2 + 9x + 20$ and 600 are each ways of representing the area of the garage with the addition, set them equal to each other and solve for x.

$$x^2 + 9x + 20 = 600$$

$$x^2 + 9x - 580 = 0$$

$$(x + 29)(x - 20) = 0$$

$$x + 29 = 0 \qquad \text{or} \qquad x - 20 = 0$$

$$x = -29 \qquad\qquad\qquad x = 20$$

Since x represents a dimension of the garage, it cannot be a negative number. Therefore, the only solution is $x = 20$.

Substitute 20 for x to find the dimensions of the garage. From the diagram above, the dimensions of the garage are $x + 4$ and $x + 5$.

$$x + 4 = \mathbf{20} + 4 \qquad x + 5 = \mathbf{20} + 5$$

$$= 24 \qquad\qquad\qquad = 25$$

The garage is 24 ft long and 25 ft wide.

© 2002 Buckle Down Publishing Company. DO NOT DUPLICATE.

1. Recall Bob's workout room from page 31. Bob will add $x^2 + 33x$ ft^2 to his workout room. If the **total** area of the workout room is now 460 ft^2, how much did Bob add to each original dimension?

```
        18            x
   ┌──────────────┬───────┐
   │              │       │
15 │     270      │  15x  │
   │              │       │
   ├──────────────┼╌╌╌╌╌╌╌┤
 x │     18x      ┊  x²   │
   └──────────────┴╌╌╌╌╌╌╌┘
```

2. Recall Louise's pool and pool deck from page 31. The area of the pool deck is represented by the binomial $3x^2 + 24x$ ft^2. If the area of the pool deck is 720 ft^2, what are the dimensions of the pool deck? What are the dimensions of the pool?

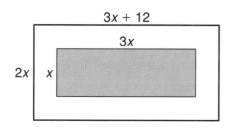

3. Recall the brothers Jack, Jeremy, and Jimmy from page 31. Jack is x years old. Jeremy is eight years less than 3 times as old as Jack. Jimmy is 2 times as old as Jeremy. Their combined ages are represented by the binomial $10x - 24$. If their combined ages are 26 years old, how old are Jack, Jeremy, and Jimmy?

© 2002 Buckle Down Publishing Company. DO NOT DUPLICATE.

Test Your Skills

1. Factor:

   $$x^2 + 8x - 20$$

   A. $(x + 4)(x - 5)$
   B. $(x + 5)(x - 4)$
   C. $(x + 10)(x - 2)$
   D. $(x + 2)(x - 10)$

2. Factor:

   $$16x^2 - 25$$

   A. $(4x - 5)(4x - 5)$
   B. $(4x + 5)(4x - 5)$
   C. $(2x - 5)(8x - 5)$
   D. $(2x + 5)(8x - 5)$

3. What is the GCF of 192 and 256?

   A. 16
   B. 32
   C. 64
   D. 72

4. Solve the following quadratic equation.

   $$12x^2 - 21x = 45$$

   A. $x = \frac{5}{4}$ and $x = 6$

   B. $x = -\frac{5}{4}$ and $x = 3$

   C. $x = -2$, $x = 0$, and $x = 9$

   D. $x = -3$, $x = 0$, and $x = 2$

5. Factor:

   $$4x^3y^3 - 2x^2y^3 + 8xy^3$$

   A. $2xy^2(2x^2y^2 - xy + 4y^2)$
   B. $2xy^3(2x + 2)(2x - 2)$
   C. $2xy^3(x - 2)(x + 1)$
   D. $2xy^3(2x^2 - x + 4)$

6. Factor:

   $$5x^4 - 65x^3 + 200x^2$$

   A. $5x^2(x - 5)(x - 8)$
   B. $5x^2(x + 4)(x - 10)$
   C. $5x^2(x^2 - 12x + 40)$
   D. $5x^2(5x^2 - 13x + 50)$

7. In the space provided below, show the steps to completely factor this trinomial.

   $$18x^3 - 51x^2 + 15x$$

© 2002 Buckle Down Publishing Company. DO NOT DUPLICATE.

Lesson 3: Rational Expressions

A rational number is a number that can be written in fractional form. A **rational expression** is an expression in fractional form where the numerator and denominator are nonzero polynomials.

Simplifying Rational Expressions

A rational expression is simplified when the numerator and denominator have no common factors other than ± 1. When you divided monomials in Lesson 1, you were simplifying rational expressions made up of monomials. To simplify a rational expression, follow these steps:

Step 1: **Completely factor the numerator and denominator.**

Step 2: **Divide any common factors from the numerator and denominator.**

Example

Simplify: $\dfrac{6x^2 - 8xy}{12x^3 + 20x^2y}$

Completely factor $6x^2 - 8xy$ and $12x^3 + 20x^2y$.

$6x^2 - 8xy = 2x(3x - 4y)$

$12x^3 + 20x^2y = 4x^2(3x + 5y)$

Divide any common factors from $2x(3x - 4y)$ and $4x^2(3x + 5y)$.

$$\frac{6x^2 - 8xy}{12x^3 + 20x^2y} = \frac{\overset{1}{\cancel{2x}}(3x - 4y)}{\underset{2}{\cancel{4x^2}}(3x + 5y)}$$

$$= \frac{3x - 4y}{2x(3x + 5y)}$$

The $3x$ in $3x - 4y$ and $2x(3x + 5y)$ cannot be divided since they are not individual factors, but parts of factors. Only whole factors can be divided.

© 2002 Buckle Down Publishing Company. DO NOT DUPLICATE.

Example

Simplify: $\dfrac{36 - x^2}{x^2 - 13x + 42}$

Completely factor $36 - x^2$ and $x^2 - 13x + 42$.

$$36 - x^2 = (6 + x)(6 - x)$$

$$x^2 - 13x + 42 = (x - 6)(x - 7)$$

Divide any common factors from $(6 + x)(6 - x)$ and $(x - 6)(x - 7)$.

$$\frac{36 - x^2}{x^2 - 13x + 42} = \frac{(6 + x)(6 - x)}{(x - 6)(x - 7)}$$

Since subtraction is not commutative, $(6 - x)$ and $(x - 6)$ are not the same. So there are no common factors as is. When you have factors like $(6 - x)$ and $(x - 6)$, factor -1 from one of them.

$$6 - x = -1(-6 + x) = -1(x - 6)$$

Now divide the common factor.

$$\frac{36 - x^2}{x^2 - 13x + 42} = \frac{(6 + x)(6 - x)}{(x - 6)(x - 7)}$$

$$= \frac{-1(6 + x)\cancel{(x - 6)}}{\cancel{(x - 6)}(x - 7)}$$

$$= -\frac{6 + x}{x - 7} \quad \left[\text{or } -\frac{x + 6}{x - 7}\right]$$

There may be some cases in which there are no common factors. If so, the rational expression is already simplified.

Example

Simplify: $\dfrac{10x^2 - 15x - 45}{24x^3 - 128x^2 + 40x}$

Completely factor $10x^2 - 15x - 45$ and $24x^3 - 128x^2 + 40x$.

$$10x^2 - 15x - 45 = 5(2x^2 - 3x - 9) = 5(x - 3)(2x + 3)$$

$$24x^3 - 128x^2 + 40x = 8x(3x^2 - 16x + 5) = 8x(x - 5)(3x - 1)$$

Divide any common factors from $5(x - 3)(2x + 3)$ and $8x(x - 5)(3x - 1)$.

$$\frac{10x^2 - 15x - 45}{24x^3 - 128x^2 + 40x} = \frac{5(x - 3)(2x + 3)}{8x(x - 5)(3x - 1)}$$

There are no common factors. This rational expression is already simplified.

© 2002 Buckle Down Publishing Company. DO NOT DUPLICATE.

Practice

Directions: For Numbers 1 through 8, simplify each rational expression.

1. $\dfrac{10x^2 - 15x}{15x^3}$

2. $\dfrac{28xy - 21y^2}{36x^2 - 27xy}$

3. $\dfrac{x^2 - 5x - 24}{x^2 + 2x - 3}$

4. $\dfrac{3x^3 - 48x}{6x^2 + 48x + 96}$

5. $\dfrac{x^4 - 5x^3 - 6x^2}{x^3 - 6x^2 - 7x}$

6. $\dfrac{2x^2 + x - 15}{4x^2 - 25}$

7. $\dfrac{3x^2 - 10x - 8}{3x^2 + 14x + 8}$

8. $\dfrac{16x^3 - 104x^2 - 56x}{12x^4 - 114x^3 - 60x^2}$

© 2002 Buckle Down Publishing Company. DO NOT DUPLICATE.

Multiplying and Dividing Rational Expressions

Rational expressions can be multiplied and divided. The steps for multiplying and dividing rational expressions will be similar to those for multiplying and dividing fractions.

Multiplying rational expressions

To multiply rational expressions, follow these steps:

Step 1: Completely factor the numerator and denominator of each expression.

Step 2: Divide any common factors that any numerator and any denominator may have.

Step 3: Multiply the numerators; multiply the denominators (straight across).

 Example

Multiply: $\dfrac{8x^2y^3}{5a} \cdot \dfrac{15a^2b}{6x^4y^2}$

Since both of the numerators and both of the denominators are monomials, they are already in factored form. Use the rules for dividing monomials to divide any common factors from any numerator and denominator.

$$\frac{8x^2y^3}{5a} \cdot \frac{15a^2b}{6x^4y^2} = \frac{\overset{4}{\cancel{8}}\cancel{x^2}\cancel{y^3}}{\underset{1}{\cancel{5}\cancel{a}}} \cdot \frac{\overset{1}{\overset{\cancel{3}}{\cancel{15}}}a^2b}{\underset{\underset{1}{\cancel{3}}}{\cancel{6}\cancel{x^{2\cancel{4}}}y^2}}$$

Multiply the remaining factors straight across.

$$= \frac{4aby}{x^2}$$

© 2002 Buckle Down Publishing Company. DO NOT DUPLICATE.

Example

Multiply: $\dfrac{6x}{x^2 + 4x - 45} \bullet \dfrac{2x^2 + 18x}{7x^2 - 35x}$

Completely factor $x^2 + 4x - 45$, $2x^2 + 18x$, and $7x^2 - 35x$.

$$\frac{6x}{x^2 + 4x - 45} \bullet \frac{2x^2 + 18x}{7x^2 - 35x} = \frac{6x}{(x + 9)(x - 5)} \bullet \frac{2x(x + 9)}{7x(x - 5)}$$

Divide the common factors from any numerator and denominator.

$$= \frac{6x}{\cancel{(x + 9)}(x - 5)} \bullet \frac{2\cancel{x}\cancel{(x + 9)}}{7\cancel{x}(x - 5)}$$

Multiply the remaining factors straight across.

$$= \frac{12x}{7(x - 5)(x - 5)}$$

Since $(x - 5)$ occurs as a factor twice, it can be written with an exponent of 2.

$$= \frac{12x}{7(x - 5)^2}$$

Practice

Directions: For Numbers 1 through 8, multiply each rational expression.

1. $\dfrac{4a^2b}{6x^2y^3} \bullet \dfrac{9x^4y}{12ab^4c}$

2. $\dfrac{5j^2k^3l^4}{8m^4n^6p} \bullet \dfrac{6mn^5p}{15j^4kl^2}$

© 2002 Buckle Down Publishing Company. DO NOT DUPLICATE.

3. $\dfrac{4x + 20}{15x - 10} \bullet \dfrac{21x - 14}{12x + 30}$

4. $\dfrac{2x^2 - 14x}{x + 3} \bullet \dfrac{x^2 - 9}{8x^3 - 56x^2}$

5. $\dfrac{x^2}{x + 4} \bullet \dfrac{2x^2 - 8}{6x^3 - 12x^2}$

6. $\dfrac{x^2 - 2x - 35}{x^2 - x - 6} \bullet \dfrac{x^2 + 2x - 15}{x^2 - 5x - 14}$

7. $\dfrac{2x^2 + 11x + 15}{4x^2 + 8x - 12} \bullet \dfrac{2x^3 - 10x^2 + 8x}{2x^2 - 7x - 30}$

8. $\dfrac{2x^2 - 6x - 80}{3x^2 - 23x - 8} \bullet \dfrac{6x^2 + 5x + 1}{6x^2 + 42x + 60}$

© 2002 Buckle Down Publishing Company. DO NOT DUPLICATE.

Dividing rational expressions

To divide rational expressions, follow these steps:

Step 1: **Rewrite the division as multiplication by the reciprocal of the divisor.**

Step 2: **Follow the steps for multiplying rational expressions.**

Example

Divide: $\dfrac{10x^2 - 13x - 3}{2x^2 + 3x - 9} \div \dfrac{2x^2 - 5x - 42}{x^2 - 3x - 18}$

Rewrite as multiplication.

$$\frac{10x^2 - 13x - 3}{2x^2 + 3x - 9} \div \frac{2x^2 - 5x - 42}{x^2 - 3x - 18} = \frac{10x^2 - 13x - 3}{2x^2 + 3x - 9} \bullet \frac{x^2 - 3x - 18}{2x^2 - 5x - 42}$$

Follow the steps for multiplying rational expressions.

$$= \frac{(2x - 3)(5x + 1)}{(x + 3)(2x - 3)} \bullet \frac{(x + 3)(x - 6)}{(x - 6)(2x + 7)}$$

$$= \frac{\cancel{(2x - 3)}(5x + 1)}{\cancel{(x + 3)}\cancel{(2x - 3)}} \bullet \frac{\cancel{(x + 3)}\cancel{(x - 6)}}{\cancel{(x - 6)}(2x + 7)}$$

$$= \frac{5x + 1}{2x + 7}$$

Practice

Directions: For Numbers 1 through 8, divide each rational expression.

1. $\dfrac{8x^4y^5z}{15j^3k^2} \div \dfrac{6x^2y^6}{5j^2k^6l}$

2. $\dfrac{4a^4b^3c}{7g^4hi^7} \div \dfrac{10a^3b^5c^2}{21g^4h^5i^2}$

© 2002 Buckle Down Publishing Company. DO NOT DUPLICATE.

3. $\dfrac{3x^3 + 2x^2}{5x^2 - 5x} \div \dfrac{18x^3 - 8x}{x^2 - 1}$

4. $\dfrac{6x^2 - 8x}{5x^3 - 6x^2} \div \dfrac{18x^3 - 24x^2}{x^4}$

5. $\dfrac{x^2 - 2x - 24}{x^2 + 10x + 21} \div \dfrac{x^2 + x - 42}{x^2 + 7x + 12}$

6. $\dfrac{2x^3 + 7x^2 - 15x}{4x^2 + 19x - 5} \div \dfrac{4x^4 - 9x^2}{8x^2 + 18x - 5}$

7. $\dfrac{x^2 - 25}{x^2 - 8x + 15} \div \dfrac{20x^2 - x - 1}{4x^2 - 13x + 3}$

8. $\dfrac{24x^2 - 6x - 45}{3x^4 - 11x^3 + 6x^2} \div \dfrac{16x^2 - 36}{3x^3 + 19x^2 - 14x}$

© 2002 Buckle Down Publishing Company. DO NOT DUPLICATE.

Adding and Subtracting Rational Expressions

Rational expressions can also be added and subtracted. The steps for adding and subtracting rational expressions are similar to those for adding and subtracting fractions.

Find the LCD of rational expressions

Before rational expressions can be added or subtracted, they need to have common denominators. To find the least common denominator (LCD) of rational expressions, follow these steps:

Step 1: **Completely factor the denominator of each expression.**

Step 2: **Find the LCM of any coefficients in the denominators.**

Step 3: **Write the product of each different factor that appears in any denominator, raised to its highest power.**

Example

Find the LCD of $\frac{3}{4a^2bc^5}$ and $\frac{5}{6a^4b^3cd^2}$.

Since both of the denominators are monomials, they are already in factored form. Find the least common multiple (LCM) of the coefficients. The LCM of 4 and 6 is 12.

The variables that appear as factors are a, b, c, and d. The highest powers of each are a^4, b^3, c^5, and d^2.

The LCD is $12a^4b^3c^5d^2$.

TIP: The LCM of two or more integers is the smallest number that is divisible by each of the numbers.

© 2002 Buckle Down Publishing Company. DO NOT DUPLICATE.

Example

Find the LCD of $\dfrac{x+9}{x^2+2x-15}$ and $\dfrac{x-3}{x^2+10x+25}$.

Completely factor $x^2+2x-15$ and $x^2+10x+25$.

$x^2+2x-15 = (x-3)(x+5)$

$x^2+10x+25 = (x+5)(x+5)$ 　　 [or $(x+5)^2$]

The different factors are $(x-3)$ and $(x+5)$. The highest power on $(x-3)$ is 1 and the highest power on $(x+5)$ is 2.

The LCD is $(x-3)(x+5)^2$.

Practice

Directions: For Numbers 1 through 8, find the LCD of the given rational expressions.

1. $\dfrac{5}{6a^4b^3}$ and $\dfrac{1}{8a^3b}$

2. $\dfrac{4d}{9x^2y}$ and $\dfrac{7d}{12x^4y^6}$

3. $\dfrac{x+2}{x-3}$ and $\dfrac{x-1}{4x-12}$

4. $\dfrac{x+4}{x+5}$ and $\dfrac{x+7}{x-3}$

5. $\dfrac{x+6}{x^2-25}$ and $\dfrac{x-1}{x^2+3x-10}$

6. $\dfrac{x-8}{x^2+6x+9}$ and $\dfrac{x+5}{x^2-4x-21}$

7. $\dfrac{2x+5}{x^2+x-30}$ and $\dfrac{3x+1}{x^2-36}$

8. $\dfrac{4x+3}{x^2-6x+5}$ and $\dfrac{5x-2}{x^2-10x+25}$

© 2002 Buckle Down Publishing Company. DO NOT DUPLICATE.

Adding and subtracting rational expressions

To add or subtract rational expressions, follow these steps:

Step 1: **Completely factor the numerator and denominator of each expression.**

Step 2: **Find the LCD of the denominators.**

Step 3: **Rewrite each expression with the LCD. Be sure to multiply each numerator by the factor(s) of the LCD that aren't in the original denominator.**

Step 4: **Multiply out each numerator. The denominators may be left in factored form.**

Step 5: **Add or subtract the numerators. Write the sum or difference over the LCD.**

Step 6: **If possible, factor the numerator. Check to be sure your answer is in simplest form.**

© 2002 Buckle Down Publishing Company. DO NOT DUPLICATE.

Example

Add: $\dfrac{3}{4a^2bc^5} + \dfrac{5}{6a^4b^3cd^2}$

Find the LCD. The LCD of $4a^2bc^5$ and $6a^4b^3cd^2$ was found on page 66 to be $12a^4b^3c^5d^2$.

Rewrite each expression as an equivalent expression with a denominator of $12a^4b^3c^5d^2$. Decide what factor each denominator was multiplied by to get $12a^4b^3c^5d^2$.

$$4a^2bc^5 \cdot \mathbf{3a^2b^2d^2} = 12a^4b^3c^5d^2$$

$$6a^4b^3cd^2 \cdot \mathbf{2c^4} = 12a^4b^3c^5d^2$$

Multiply each numerator of the same expression by the same factor.

$$\frac{3}{4a^2bc^5} + \frac{5}{6a^4b^3cd^2} = \frac{3 \cdot \mathbf{3a^2b^2d^2}}{12a^4b^3c^5d^2} + \frac{5 \cdot \mathbf{2c^4}}{12a^4b^3c^5d^2}$$

Multiply out each numerator.

$$= \frac{9a^2b^2d^2}{12a^4b^3c^5d^2} + \frac{10c^4}{12a^4b^3c^5d^2}$$

Add $9a^2b^2d^2$ and $10c^4$. Since these are not like terms they cannot be combined.

$$= \frac{\mathbf{9a^2b^2d^2 + 10c^4}}{\mathbf{12a^4b^3c^5d^2}}$$

Since $9a^2b^2d^2 + 10c^4$ cannot be factored, the expression is in simplest form.

© 2002 Buckle Down Publishing Company. DO NOT DUPLICATE.

Example

Subtract: $\dfrac{x + 9}{x^2 + 2x - 15} - \dfrac{x - 3}{x^2 + 10x + 25}$

Find the LCD. The LCD of $x^2 + 2x - 15$ and $x^2 + 10x + 25$ was found on page 67 to be $(x - 3)(x + 5)^2$.

Rewrite each expression as an equivalent expression with a denominator of $(x - 3)(x + 5)^2$. Decide what factor each denominator was multiplied by to get $(x - 3)(x + 5)^2$.

$$(x - 3)(x + 5)\mathbf{(x + 5)} = (x - 3)(x + 5)^2$$

$$(x + 5)^2\mathbf{(x - 3)} = (x - 3)(x + 5)^2$$

Multiply each numerator of the same expression by the same factor.

$$\frac{x + 9}{x^2 + 2x - 15} - \frac{x - 3}{x^2 + 10x + 25} = \frac{(x + 9)\mathbf{(x + 5)}}{(x - 3)(x + 5)^2} - \frac{(x - 3)\mathbf{(x - 3)}}{(x - 3)(x + 5)^2}$$

Multiply out each numerator.

$$= \frac{x^2 + 14x + 45}{(x - 3)(x + 5)^2} - \frac{x^2 - 6x + 9}{(x - 3)(x + 5)^2}$$

Subtract $x^2 - 6x + 9$ from $x^2 + 14x + 45$. Change $-$ to $+$ and each term of $x^2 - 6x + 9$ to its opposite. Then add the like terms. Write the sum over $(x - 3)(x + 5)^2$.

$$= \frac{x^2 + 14x + 45 - (x^2 - 6x + 9)}{(x - 3)(x + 5)^2}$$

$$= \frac{x^2 + 14x + 45 + (-x^2) + 6x - 9}{(x - 3)(x + 5)^2}$$

$$= \frac{20x + 36}{(x - 3)(x + 5)^2}$$

If possible, factor $20x + 36$.

$$= \frac{\mathbf{4(5x + 9)}}{\mathbf{(x - 3)(x + 5)^2}}$$

There are no common factors in the numerator and denominator. The expression is in simplest form.

© 2002 Buckle Down Publishing Company. DO NOT DUPLICATE.

Practice

Directions: For Numbers 1 through 8, add or subtract each rational expression.

1. $\dfrac{5}{6x^2y^3} - \dfrac{3}{8x^4z^2}$

2. $\dfrac{x + 5}{x - 6} + \dfrac{3x + 1}{2x - 3}$

3. $\dfrac{x + 2}{x + 3} - \dfrac{x - 2}{x - 5}$

4. $\dfrac{x - 3}{x^2 - 11x + 18} + \dfrac{x + 5}{x^2 - 4}$

© 2002 Buckle Down Publishing Company. DO NOT DUPLICATE.

5. $\dfrac{4y}{5x^2} + \dfrac{7x}{6y^2}$

6. $\dfrac{4x - 3}{x - 4} - \dfrac{x + 6}{x + 2}$

7. $\dfrac{x + 4}{3x - 6} + \dfrac{x + 1}{6x - 18}$

8. $\dfrac{4x - 1}{x^2 - 9x - 10} - \dfrac{2x + 3}{x^2 - 5x - 50}$

© 2002 Buckle Down Publishing Company. DO NOT DUPLICATE.

Test Your Skills

1. Add:

$$\frac{x - 5}{x + 4} + \frac{2x - 9}{3x - 5}$$

  A. $\dfrac{5x^2 - 21x - 11}{(x + 4)(3x - 5)}$

  B. $\dfrac{3x - 14}{(x + 4)(3x - 5)}$

  C. $\dfrac{3x^2 - 18x + 14}{x + 4}$

  D. $\dfrac{4x - 7}{3x - 5}$

2. Divide:

$$\frac{x^2 - x - 12}{x^2 + 9x + 18} \div \frac{x^2 - 2x - 8}{x^2 - x - 42}$$

  A. $\dfrac{x + 3}{x + 6}$

  B. $\dfrac{x - 7}{x + 2}$

  C. $\dfrac{x - 4}{x + 2}$

  D. $\dfrac{x - 7}{x + 6}$

3. Simplify:

$$\frac{12x^3 - 92x^2 - 32x}{6x^4 - 24x^3 - 192x^2}$$

  A. $\dfrac{2(3x + 1)}{3x(x + 4)}$

  B. $\dfrac{2x(x - 8)}{3x^2(x + 8)}$

  C. $\dfrac{x(3x - 4)}{x^2(x + 16)}$

  D. $\dfrac{x + 2}{x(x - 2)}$

4. What is the LCD of the following rational expressions?

$$\frac{x - 4}{x^2 - 8x + 16} \text{ and } \frac{x + 3}{2x^2 - x - 28}$$

  A. $(2x + 7)(x - 4)(x + 4)$

  B. $(2x - 7)(x - 4)(x + 4)$

  C. $(2x - 7)(x + 4)^2$

  D. $(2x + 7)(x - 4)^2$

5. Multiply:

$$\frac{2x^2 - x - 10}{3x^2 + 5x - 28} \bullet \frac{x^2 + 10x + 24}{x^2 + 8x + 12}$$

  A. $\dfrac{2x - 5}{x + 6}$

  B. $\dfrac{x + 2}{x + 6}$

  C. $\dfrac{2x - 5}{3x - 7}$

  D. $\dfrac{x + 2}{3x - 7}$

6. In the space provided below, show the steps needed to subtract these rational expressions.

$$\frac{x + 5}{2x - 10} - \frac{x - 2}{4x - 12}$$

© 2002 Buckle Down Publishing Company. DO NOT DUPLICATE.

Lesson 4: Patterns

You use patterns to investigate relationships and to solve problems. Once you find the rule for a pattern, you can describe, extend, or analyze it. You can also use the rule as the basis for creating new patterns. Sequences and series are the most common types of patterns you will come across.

Rules for Patterns

To find the rule for a number pattern, you need to discover the operation or operations used. In some patterns, the rule is to add. In others, it is to subtract, multiply, or divide. The rule might even include a combination of •operations.

 Example

What is the rule for the following number pattern?

1, 5, 9, 13, 17, 21, . . .

You need to find what you have to do to each number to get the next number in the pattern.

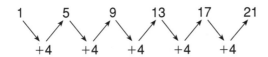

The rule is "add 4." This can also be written as +4.

 Example

What is the rule for this number pattern?

5, 15, 45, 135, 405, 1,215, . . .

You need to find what you have to do to each number to get the next number in the pattern.

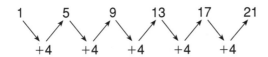

The rule is "multiply by 3." This can also be written as •3.

© 2002 Buckle Down Publishing Company. DO NOT DUPLICATE.

Example

What is the rule for the following number pattern? This pattern is a little different than the others. Look closely.

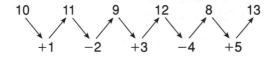

The rule is "add 1, subtract 2, add 3, subtract 4, add 5, and so on." This can also be written as +1, −2, +3, −4, +5, . . .

Practice

Directions: For Numbers 1 through 6, write the next three terms of the pattern. Then write the rule for the pattern.

1. 1, 7, 13, 19, 25, _____, _____, _____

   rule: _____

2. 3,200, 1,600, 800, 400, 200, _____, _____, _____

   rule: _____

3. 95, 84, 73, 62, 51, _____, _____, _____

   rule: _____

4. 3, 12, 48, 192, 768, _____, _____, _____

   rule: _____

5. 56, 58, 55, 57, 54, 56, 53, _____, _____, _____

   rule: _____

6. 84, 21, 168, 42, 336, 84, 672, _____, _____, _____

   rule: _____

© 2002 Buckle Down Publishing Company. DO NOT DUPLICATE.

Sequences

A **sequence** has terms that are arranged in a certain order. Sequences are either finite or infinite.

In a **finite** sequence, you can count the number of terms in the sequence.

1, 4, 7, 10, 13 is a finite sequence that has five terms.

In an **infinite** sequence, you can't count the number of terms. The sequence goes on forever.

1, 4, 7, 10, 13, . . . is an infinite sequence.

↑

(The three-dot notation means *and so on*.)

The *n*th term

Notation such as $a_1, a_2, a_3, \ldots, a_n$ is used to represent the terms of a sequence. The **subscripts** identify the position of the terms in the sequence.

term in the sequence → a_1

↑

subscript indicates position

a_1 represents the **1st** term in the sequence.

a_2 represents the **2nd** term in the sequence.

a_3 represents the **3rd** term in the sequence.

.
.
.

a_n represents the **nth** term in the sequence.

The *n*th term of a sequence is denoted by a_n where n represents the position of the term in the sequence. The *n*th term can be any term.

© 2002 Buckle Down Publishing Company. DO NOT DUPLICATE.

Arithmetic sequences

An **arithmetic sequence** is a sequence of numbers where the **difference** between consecutive terms is **constant**. This is called the **common difference (d)**.

Example

2, 5, 8, 11, 14, . . .   This is an increasing arithmetic sequence with a common difference of 3.

32, 26, 20, 14, 8, . . .   This is a decreasing arithmetic sequence with a common difference of –6.

Recursive definition

A **recursive definition** describes a sequence whose terms are defined by one or more preceding terms. Known terms are used to calculate new terms. New terms become known terms and are used to calculate further new terms.

Use the following formula to find any term of an arithmetic sequence. (a_{n-1} is the term immediately preceding a_n.)

$$a_1$$
$$a_n = (a_{n-1}) + d \ \text{ for } \ n > 1$$

Example

What are the next three terms (a_5, a_6, a_7) of the following sequence?

1, 5, 9, 13, . . .

Use the following formula.

$$a_1 = 1$$
$$a_n = (a_{n-1}) + 4 \ \text{ for } \ n > 1$$

$a_5 = (a_{5-1}) + 4 = a_4 + 4 = 13 + 4 = \textbf{17}$ (5th term)

$a_6 = (a_{6-1}) + 4 = a_5 + 4 = 17 + 4 = \textbf{21}$ (6th term)

$a_7 = (a_{7-1}) + 4 = a_6 + 4 = 21 + 4 = \textbf{25}$ (7th term)

The next three terms of the sequence are 17, 21, and 25.

© 2002 Buckle Down Publishing Company. DO NOT DUPLICATE.

Explicit definition

The **explicit definition** allows us to calculate any term in a sequence in a direct way using the first term and the common difference between terms. The explicit definition can also be used to solve real-world problems.

Use the following formula to find any term of an arithmetic sequence.

$$a_n = a_1 + (n-1)d$$

Example

What are the 10th, 25th, and 50th terms of the following sequence?

1, 5, 9, 13, . . .

Use this formula: $a_n = a_1 + (n-1)d$

$a_{10} = 1 + (10-1) \bullet 4 = 1 + (9) \bullet 4 = 1 + 36 = \mathbf{37}$ (10th term)

$a_{25} = 1 + (25-1) \bullet 4 = 1 + (24) \bullet 4 = 1 + 96 = \mathbf{97}$ (25th term)

$a_{50} = 1 + (50-1) \bullet 4 = 1 + (49) \bullet 4 = 1 + 196 = \mathbf{197}$ (50th term)

The 10th term is 37, the 25th term is 97, and the 50th term is 197.

Example

Starting May 1, a new store will begin giving away 500 posters as a promotion. Each day, 4 posters will be given away. If the store is open 7 days a week, how many posters will the store have left when it opens on May 14?

Day of Promotion	1	2	3	4
Posters Remaining	500	496	492	488

Use the following formula.

$$a_n = a_1 + (n-1)d$$

In this example, $a_1 = 500$, $n = 14$, and $d = -4$.

$a_{14} = 500 + (14-1) \bullet (-4)$

$= 500 + 13 \bullet (-4)$

$= 500 - 52$

$= 448$

When it opens on May 14, the store will have 448 posters left.

© 2002 Buckle Down Publishing Company. DO NOT DUPLICATE.

Practice

Directions: For Numbers 1 through 3, find the next three terms of the sequence.

1. 3, 10, 17, 24, 31, _____, _____, _____

2. 34, 31, 28, 25, 22, _____, _____, _____

3. 10.5, 11.1, 11.7, 12.3, 12.9, _____, _____, _____

Directions: For Numbers 4 through 6, find the given terms of the sequence.

4. 53, 50, 47, 44, 41, . . .

$a_{15} =$ _____ $a_{25} =$ _____ $a_{50} =$ _____

5. 25, 40, 55, 70, 85, . . .

$a_{20} =$ _____ $a_{50} =$ _____ $a_{100} =$ _____

6. 88, 81, 74, 67, 60, . . .

$a_{75} =$ _____ $a_{150} =$ _____ $a_{225} =$ _____

7. Aaron gets a starting hourly wage of $8.50 and annual raises of $0.35. What will Aaron's hourly wage be during his tenth year?

8. A pile of bricks has 97 bricks in the first row, 91 bricks in the second row, 85 bricks in the third row, and so on until there is only one brick in the top row. How many bricks are in the 15th row?

© 2002 Buckle Down Publishing Company. DO NOT DUPLICATE.

Geometric sequences

A **geometric sequence** is a sequence of numbers where the **ratio** of consecutive terms is constant. This ratio is called the **common ratio (r)**. Sometimes the terms of a geometric sequence get so large that you may need to express the terms in scientific notation rounded to the nearest tenth.

 Example

2, 6, 18, 54, . . .   This is an increasing geometric sequence with a common ratio of 3.

1,000, 200, 40, 8, . . .   This is a decreasing geometric sequence with a common ratio of 0.2 or $\frac{1}{5}$.

Recursive definition

Use the following formula to find any term of a geometric sequence. (a_{n-1} is the term immediately preceding a_n.)

$$a_1$$
$$a_n = (a_{n-1}) \cdot r \quad \text{for } n > 1$$

 Example

What are the next three terms (a_5, a_6, a_7) of the following sequence?

4, 20, 100, 500, . . .

Use the following formula.

$$a_1 = 4$$
$$a_n = (a_{n-1}) \cdot 5 \quad \text{for } n > 1$$

$$\boldsymbol{a_5} = (a_{5-1}) \cdot 5 = a_4 \cdot 5 = 500 \cdot 5 = \mathbf{2,500} \quad \text{(5th term)}$$
$$\boldsymbol{a_6} = (a_{6-1}) \cdot 5 = a_5 \cdot 5 = 2,500 \cdot 5 = \mathbf{12,500} \quad \text{(6th term)}$$
$$\boldsymbol{a_7} = (a_{7-1}) \cdot 5 = a_6 \cdot 5 = 12,500 \cdot 5 = \mathbf{62,500} \quad \text{(7th term)}$$

The next three terms of the sequence are 2,500, 12,500, and 62,500.

© 2002 Buckle Down Publishing Company. DO NOT DUPLICATE.

Explicit definition

Use the following formula to find any term of a geometric sequence. The explicit definition can also be used to solve real-world problems.

$$a_n = a_1 r^{(n-1)}$$

 Example

What are the 10th, 25th, and 50th terms of the following sequence? Express the terms in scientific notation rounded to the nearest tenth.

4, 20, 100, 500, . . .

Use this formula: $a_n = a_1 r^{(n-1)}$

$a_{10} = 4 \bullet 5^{(10-1)} = 4 \bullet 5^9 = \mathbf{7.8 \bullet 10^6}$ (10th term)

$a_{25} = 4 \bullet 5^{(25-1)} = 4 \bullet 5^{24} = \mathbf{2.4 \bullet 10^{17}}$ (25th term)

$a_{50} = 4 \bullet 5^{(50-1)} = 4 \bullet 5^{49} = \mathbf{7.1 \bullet 10^{34}}$ (50th term)

The 10th term is $7.8 \bullet 10^6$, the 25th term is $2.4 \bullet 10^{17}$, and the 50th term is $7.1 \bullet 10^{34}$.

Example

Ralph's new job has a starting salary of $20,000. Find his salary during his fourth year on the job if he receives annual raises of 5%.

If we let a_1 = Ralph's first-year salary, then the next year, his salary will be $a_1 + 0.05a_1$, or $1.05a_1$. Ralph's yearly salaries will form a geometric sequence with a common ratio of 1.05.

Use the following formula.

$$a_n = a_1(r)^{n-1}$$

In this example, $a_1 = 20{,}000$, $r = 1.05$, and $n = 4$.

$a_4 = 20{,}000(1.05)^{4-1}$

$\quad = 20{,}000(1.05)^3$

$\quad = 20{,}000(1.157625)$

$\quad = 23{,}152.50$

Ralph's fourth-year salary will be $23,152.50.

© 2002 Buckle Down Publishing Company. DO NOT DUPLICATE.

Practice

Directions: For Numbers 1 through 3, find the next three terms of the sequence.

1. 1, 3, 9, 27, 81, _____, _____, _____

2. 128, 64, 32, 16, 8, _____, _____, _____

3. 0.1, 0.4, 1.6, 6.4, 25.6, _____, _____, _____

Directions: For Numbers 4 through 6, find the given terms of the sequence. (Express the terms in scientific notation rounded to the nearest tenth.)

4. 0.01, 0.1, 1, 10, 100, . . .

     $a_{15} =$ _____ $a_{30} =$ _____ $a_{50} =$ _____

5. 1, 6, 36, 216, 1,296, . . .

     $a_{12} =$ _____ $a_{18} =$ _____ $a_{24} =$ _____

6. 1, –2, 4, –8, 16, . . .

     $a_{20} =$ _____ $a_{35} =$ _____ $a_{50} =$ _____

7. The value of Lynn's car depreciates at about 15% per year. If Lynn purchased her car for $21,900, what will its value be in ten years? (Round your answer to the nearest dollar.)

8. When Roger was 10 years old, he bought a dozen baseball cards to start a collection. Each year, he bought twice as many cards as the year before. How many baseball cards did Roger buy when he was 15 years old?

© 2002 Buckle Down Publishing Company. DO NOT DUPLICATE.

Series

A **series** is the sum of the terms of a sequence.

Arithmetic series

An **arithmetic series** is the sum of the terms of an arithmetic sequence.

Example

What series does the following sequence represent?

2, 5, 8, 11, 14, . . .

Add the terms of the sequence to find the series.

2 + 5 + 8 + 11 + 14 + . . .

The Greek letter *sigma* (Σ) is used to indicate a series. The Σ is sometimes called a summation sign. The summation sign and the explicit definition of an arithmetic sequence are used below to represent the sum of the first 50 terms of the series from the example above.

$$\sum_{n=1}^{50} [2 + 3(n - 1)]$$

The explicit definition of the sequence $[2 + 3(n - 1)]$ is called the **summand**. The variable (n) is called the **index**. The expressions ($n = 1$ and 50) above and below the Σ indicate where you begin and end in your substitution for values of n. The index does not always start at 1, so before you begin, look at the value of the index. This series is found by adding the 50 terms of the sequence starting with $n = 1$ and ending with $n = 50$.

$$\sum_{n=1}^{50} [2 + 3(n - 1)] = 2 + 5 + 8 + \ldots + 143 + 146 + 149$$

© 2002 Buckle Down Publishing Company. DO NOT DUPLICATE.

Two series that have different notation can represent the same sequence. Look very closely at the terms of the series to see if the two series represent the same sequence.

Example

Do these two series represent the same sequence?

$$\sum_{n=0}^{3} 3n \ \text{ and } \ \sum_{k=7}^{10} \frac{1}{2}(6k - 42)$$

Write the terms of the two series.

$$\sum_{n=0}^{3} 3n = 0 + 3 + 6 + 9$$

$$\sum_{k=7}^{10} \frac{1}{2}(6k - 42) = 0 + 3 + 6 + 9$$

The two series represent the same sequence.

Practice

Directions: For Numbers 1 through 3, write whether the given two series represent the same sequence.

1. $\sum_{n=0}^{4} (6n + 35) \ \text{ and } \ \sum_{k=5}^{9} (5 + 6k)$

2. $\sum_{x=1}^{5} (12x - 7) \ \text{ and } \ \sum_{y=4}^{8} (12y - 43)$

3. $\sum_{r=0}^{3} (13 - 3r) \ \text{ and } \ \sum_{h=1}^{4} \frac{1}{2}(26 - 6h)$

© 2002 Buckle Down Publishing Company. DO NOT DUPLICATE.

Directions: For Numbers 4 through 10, write the first three terms and the last three terms of the series. Use the three-dot notation (. . .) where appropriate. Do not find the sum.

4. $$\sum_{n=1}^{17} (9n - 8) =$$

5. $$\sum_{k=7}^{12} 6k =$$

6. $$\sum_{x=1}^{74} -3(x - 6) =$$

7. $$\sum_{m=1}^{20} 5(5 - m) =$$

8. $$\sum_{t=5}^{10} 16(t - 1) =$$

9. $$\sum_{p=0}^{25} 7(4 - p) =$$

10. $$\sum_{g=1}^{50} 10g =$$

© 2002 Buckle Down Publishing Company. DO NOT DUPLICATE.

Evaluating arithmetic series

To evaluate a finite arithmetic series, find the sum. If a series is made up of only a few terms, the sum is easy to compute. But what about a series with 50 terms? Finding that sum would be very time consuming. Luckily there is a **theorem** (proven statement) that makes this process easier for any finite arithmetic series.

The sum (S) of the first n terms of a finite arithmetic series is found by solving the following formula.

$$S_n = \frac{n(a_1 + a_n)}{2}$$

In the formula, $\boldsymbol{a_1}$ is the 1st term of the series

$\boldsymbol{a_n}$ is the nth term

Example

Evaluate the following series.

$$\sum_{n=1}^{12} (9n + 2)$$

Find the values of a_1 and a_{12}.

$a_1 = 9(1) + 2 = 11$

$a_{12} = 9(12) + 2 = 110$

Substitute the values of n, a_1, and a_{12} into the formula and solve.

$$S_{12} = \frac{12(11 + 110)}{2}$$

$$= \frac{1,452}{2}$$

$$= 726$$

$$\sum_{n=1}^{12} (9n + 2) = 726$$

© 2002 Buckle Down Publishing Company. DO NOT DUPLICATE.

You cannot find the sum of an infinite series, but you can find the sum of the first n terms of an infinite series.

Example

Find the sum of the first 25 terms of the following arithmetic series.

$$3 + 7 + 11 + 15 + \ldots$$

The first term is 3. Find the value of a_{25} by using the explicit definition of the arithmetic sequence that makes up the series.

$$a_n = a_1 + (n - 1)d \text{ where } n = 25, a_1 = 3, \text{ and } d = 4$$

$$a_{25} = 3 + (25 - 1)4$$

$$a_{25} = 99$$

Substitute the values for n, a_1, and a_{25} into the formula and solve.

$$S_{25} = \frac{25(3 + 99)}{2}$$

$$= \frac{2{,}550}{2}$$

$$= 1{,}275$$

The sum of the first 25 terms of the arithmetic series $3 + 7 + 11 + 15 + \ldots$ is 1,275.

Practice

1. Find the sum of the first 10 terms of the following arithmetic series.

$$1 + 7 + 13 + 19 + \ldots$$

2. Find the sum of the first 40 terms of the following arithmetic series.

$$-1 + (-3) + (-5) + (-7) + \ldots$$

© 2002 Buckle Down Publishing Company. DO NOT DUPLICATE.

Directions: For Numbers 3 through 6, evaluate the series.

3. $$\sum_{k=1}^{40} (2k + 2)$$

4. $$\sum_{g=1}^{15} (10 - 2g)$$

5. $$\sum_{z=5}^{20} -5z$$

6. $$\sum_{f=0}^{50} (4f - 100)$$

Directions: For Numbers 7 and 8, use the formula for finding the sum of the terms of a series. Show your work.

7. The front row of a school's auditorium has 15 seats. Each of the remaining 49 rows has 2 more seats than the row ahead of it. How many seats are there in the auditorium?

8. Jen opened a savings account and deposited $25 during the first month. Each month she will deposit 10 more dollars into her account than in the preceding month. How much money will Jen have deposited into her savings account after 2 years?

© 2002 Buckle Down Publishing Company. DO NOT DUPLICATE.

Geometric series

A **geometric series** is the sum of the terms of a geometric sequence. Two series that have different notation can represent the same sequence.

Example

What series does the following sequence represent?

$$1, 2, 4, 8, 16, \ldots$$

Add the terms of the sequence to find the series.

$$1 + 2 + 4 + 8 + 16 + \ldots$$

The summation sign and the explicit definition of a geometric sequence are used below to represent the sum of the first 15 terms of the series from the example above.

$$\sum_{n=1}^{15} 2^{(n-1)}$$

This series is found by adding the first 15 terms of the sequence.

$$\sum_{n=1}^{15} 2^{(n-1)} = 1 + 2 + 4 + \ldots + 4{,}096 + 8{,}192 + 16{,}384$$

Practice

Directions: For Numbers 1 and 2, write whether the given two series represent the same sequence.

1. $\displaystyle\sum_{n=1}^{5} 4^{(n-1)}$ and $\displaystyle\sum_{k=0}^{4} 2^{(2k-1)}$

2. $\displaystyle\sum_{n=1}^{4} \left(\frac{1}{2}\right)^{n}$ and $\displaystyle\sum_{h=0}^{3} \frac{1}{2^{(h+1)}}$

© 2002 Buckle Down Publishing Company. DO NOT DUPLICATE.

Directions: For Numbers 3 through 9, write the first three terms and the last three terms of the series. Use the three-dot notation (. . .) where appropriate. Do not find the sum.

3. $\displaystyle\sum_{j=1}^{17} 2^j =$

4. $\displaystyle\sum_{k=5}^{10} [-5]^{(k-1)} =$

5. $\displaystyle\sum_{x=0}^{5} \left(\frac{1}{3}\right)^{2x} =$

6. $\displaystyle\sum_{m=20}^{30} 10^{(25-m)} =$

7. $\displaystyle\sum_{t=5}^{10} \frac{-1}{4^{(t-4)}} =$

8. $\displaystyle\sum_{p=0}^{5} [2 \bullet 2^{(5-p)}] =$

9. $\displaystyle\sum_{d=9}^{17} 3^{(d-9)} =$

© 2002 Buckle Down Publishing Company. DO NOT DUPLICATE.

Evaluating geometric series

There is also a theorem that can be used to find the sum of a finite geometric series.

The sum (S) of the first n terms of a finite geometric series is found by solving the following formula.

$$S_n = \frac{a_1(1 - r^n)}{1 - r}$$

In the formula, a_1 is the 1st term of the series

r is the common ratio such that $r \neq 1$

(If $r = 1$, then $S_n = na_1$.)

 Example

Evaluate the following series.

$$\sum_{n=1}^{5} 9 \bullet 5^{(n - 1)}$$

Find the values of a_1 and r^n.

$a_1 = 9 \bullet 5^{(1 - 1)} = 9$

$r^n = 5^5 = 3{,}125$

Substitute the values of a_1, r^n, and r into the formula and solve.

$$S_5 = \frac{9(1 - 3{,}125)}{1 - 5}$$

$$= \frac{-28{,}116}{-4}$$

$$= 7{,}029$$

$$\sum_{n=1}^{5} 9 \bullet 5^{(n - 1)} = 7{,}029$$

© 2002 Buckle Down Publishing Company. DO NOT DUPLICATE.

Example

Find the sum of the first 8 terms of the following geometric series.

$$5 + 15 + 45 + \ldots$$

The first term is 5. Find the value of r by dividing any two consecutive terms, then find the value of r^n.

$$r = 15 \div 5 = 3$$

$$r^n = 3^8 = 6{,}561$$

Substitute the values of a_1, r^n, and r into the formula and solve.

$$S_8 = \frac{5(1 - 6{,}561)}{1 - 3}$$

$$= \frac{-32{,}800}{-2}$$

$$= 16{,}400$$

The sum of the first 8 terms of the geometric series $5 + 15 + 45 + \ldots$ is 16,400.

Practice

1. Find the sum of the first 10 terms of the following geometric series.

$$5 + 15 + 45 + 135 + \ldots$$

2. Find the sum of the first 20 terms of the following geometric series.

$$1 + (-2) + 4 + (-8) + \ldots$$

3. Find the sum of the first 12 terms of the following geometric series.

$$1 + 2 + 4 + 8 + \ldots$$

© 2002 Buckle Down Publishing Company. DO NOT DUPLICATE.

Directions: For Numbers 4 through 7, evaluate the series.

4. $$\sum_{n=1}^{4} \frac{1}{2} \bullet 4^{(n-1)}$$

5. $$\sum_{m=1}^{8} 2^{(m-1)}$$

6. $$\sum_{k=0}^{15} \left[-\frac{1}{4}\right]^{(k+1)}$$

7. $$\sum_{x=5}^{25} 10^{(x-5)}$$

Directions: For Numbers 8 and 9, use the formula for finding the sum of the terms of a series. Show your work.

8. Pete has been renting an apartment for the past 8 years. During the first year of rental, he paid $400 a month. Each year thereafter, his rent was increased by 5%. What is the total amount of money Pete has paid for rent over the last 8 years? (Round your answer to the nearest dollar.)

9. The management of a theater company consists of a president, 4 vice-presidents, 16 managers, and so on. There are a total of 5 levels of management. How many people are involved in the 5 levels?

© 2002 Buckle Down Publishing Company. DO NOT DUPLICATE.

Predictions

A **prediction** is an informed guess about the future value of something based on observation, experience, or reasoning. You can use what you know about sequences and series to make predictions. However, you also need to consider whether a prediction is **reasonable** (makes sense) in a given situation.

Example

A wholesale boot company promises to deliver orders of a special line of handmade boots according to the schedule below.

Delivery Schedule

Size of Order	5 pairs or fewer	6–10 pairs	11–15 pairs	16–20 pairs
Delivery Time	4 weeks or less	6 weeks or less	8 weeks or less	

Is it reasonable to make a prediction about what delivery time the company would most likely promise for an order of 18 pairs of handmade boots?

It is reasonable to make a prediction. The delivery time for boots seems clearly to depend on the number of pairs ordered. Based on the information from the table, the delivery time would be 10 weeks or less.

Example

Kurt received the following scores on his first three math tests this semester.

Kurt's Test Scores

Test	1	2	3	4
Score	76	82	88	

Is it reasonable to make a prediction about his score on the fourth test?

It is not reasonable to predict Kurt's fourth test score with any accuracy. Even though he has been scoring six points higher with each test he takes, there is little reason to believe that he will score a 94 on his next test. There are too many variables to consider, such as the material being covered, the overall difficulty of the test, Kurt's preparation for the test, and so on.

© 2002 Buckle Down Publishing Company. DO NOT DUPLICATE.

Practice

1. The following table compares pizza prices at four different restaurants.

12" Pizza Prices

Restaurant A	Restaurant B	Restaurant C	Restaurant D	Restaurant E
$7.99	$8.99	$9.50	$8.99	

Is it reasonable to predict what Restaurant E's price is for a 12" pizza? Explain.

_____

_____

_____

2. This sign was placed near a rack of T-shirts in a clothing store.

BUY 1 T-shirt   pay $14.99

BUY 2 T-shirts   pay $26.98   Save $3   off the

BUY 3 T-shirts   pay $38.97   Save $6   regular

BUY 4 T-shirts   pay $50.96   Save $9   price

BUY 5 T-shirts

If reasonable, predict how much 5 shirts cost and how much you would save by buying 5 shirts at the sale price as opposed to the regular price.

_____

_____

_____

© 2002 Buckle Down Publishing Company. DO NOT DUPLICATE.

Decisions

A **decision** is a conclusion arrived at after careful consideration of all of the information.

Example

Stephanie is buying a car. The car dealership offers her two ways to pay for the car.

Option I. Put $899 down and make payments of $330 per month for 3 years.

Option II. Put $199 down and make payments of $375 per month for 3 years.

Which way should Stephanie decide to pay for the car?

This decision is a lot harder than it seems. There are several factors involved in making the final decision. For example, how much money does Stephanie have saved to put down and how much can she afford to make in monthly payments? These are two important questions that must be weighed very carefully before the final decision can be made.

Stephanie's decision will be based only on paying the least amount of money to the dealership. The following calculations show how much money she would pay to the dealership for each option.

Write the two options as arithmetic sequences, then solve for the 37th month (the first month is the down payment, then there are 36 more months of payments).

Option I. $a_n = a_1 + (n - 1)d$ where $a_1 = 899$ and $d = 330$

$a_{37} = 899 + (37 - 1)330$

$a_{37} = 12{,}779$

Option II. $a_n = a_1 + (n - 1)d$ where $a_1 = 199$ and $d = 375$

$a_{37} = 199 + (37 - 1)375$

$a_{37} = 13{,}699$

Since Stephanie's final decision is based on paying the least amount of money to the dealership, payment Option I is the better decision.

© 2002 Buckle Down Publishing Company. DO NOT DUPLICATE.

Practice

1. Mark is trying to decide which rental car agency to use while he is away on business. He has called two different agencies and has been given the following quotes on rental fees.

Rental Car Agencies' Charges

Rent-A-Reck	Lease-A-Lemon
$49.99 per day + $0.60 per mile	$25.99 per day + $1.34 per mile

Mark plans on driving 35 miles a day. Based on finances alone, which rental car agency offers the better deal? How much will he save by using that rental car agency?

_____

_____

_____

_____

_____

© 2002 Buckle Down Publishing Company. DO NOT DUPLICATE.

2. Suppose someone told you that you had won a special lottery that pays you in increasing increments in one of two ways:

Option I.   The lottery officials will give you $3 the first year. At the start of the second year, they will give you $6 (for a total of $9 received). At the start of the third year, they will give you $18. At the start of the fourth year, they will give you $54, and so on.

Option II.   The lottery officials will give you $100 the first year. At the start of the second year, they will give you $100 (for a total of $200 received). At the start of the third year, they will give you $200. At the start of the fourth year, they will give you $400, and so on.

This table shows the total amount of money received for the first five years.

Lottery Payments

Year		1	2	3	4	5
Total Amount of Money Received	I	3	9	27	81	243
	II	100	200	400	800	1,600

Based solely on the amount of money you will receive without interest, which way should you decide to receive your lottery money? Explain your answer.

_____

_____

_____

_____

© 2002 Buckle Down Publishing Company. DO NOT DUPLICATE.

Test Your Skills

1. What is the rule for this pattern?

   $$-1, 0, -1, 0, -1$$

   A. add -1, subtract -1
   B. add 1, subtract 1
   C. add -1, subtract 1
   D. add 1, subtract -1

2. Evaluate:

   $$\sum_{w=1}^{9} 4 \cdot 3^{(w-1)}$$

   A. 1,456
   B. 4,372
   C. 13,120
   D. 39,364

3. In the space provided below, find the 100th term in the following sequence. Show your work, including the formula you use.

   $$3, 7, 11, 15, 19, \ldots$$

4. Evaluate:

   $$\sum_{n=1}^{55} (3n + 8)$$

   A. 5,060
   B. 4,875
   C. 4,624
   D. 4,498

5. Which expression represents the number of dots in a triangle with n dots on the bottom?

   A. $2n + 1$
   B. $2n + n$
   C. $2n - 1$
   D. $0.5n(n + 1)$

6. A projectile fired vertically upward rises 1,500 feet in the first second, 1,450 feet the following second, 1,400 feet the third second, and so on. How many feet does it rise in the 20th second?

   A. 600
   B. 550
   C. 500
   D. 450

© 2002 Buckle Down Publishing Company. DO NOT DUPLICATE.

7. What is the next number in this pattern?

   10, 12, 11, 13, 12, 14, . . .

   A. 10
   B. 12
   C. 13
   D. 16

8. Starting with $n = 1$, what are the first 5 terms of the following sequence?

   $$a_n = 6n + 5$$

   A. 1, 2, 3, 4, 5
   B. 5, 11, 17, 23, 29
   C. 11, 17, 23, 29, 35
   D. 17, 23, 29, 35, 41

9. An intern at a publishing company is offered a $10,000 starting salary with an annual raise of $800. If she is still there in year 10, what will her salary be?

   A. $15,600
   B. $16,400
   C. $17,200
   D. $18,000

10. What is the 25th term in the following sequence?

    0.15, 1.5, 15, 150, . . .

    A. $1.5 \cdot 10^{23}$
    B. $1.5 \cdot 10^{24}$
    C. $1.5 \cdot 10^{25}$
    D. $1.5 \cdot 10^{26}$

11. Evaluate:

    $$\sum_{n=1}^{6} \frac{1}{5} \bullet 5^{(n-1)}$$

    A. 695.4
    B. 781.2
    C. 863.8
    D. 943.6

12. Wendy bought 2 stamps during her first year of stamp collecting. Each year, she is going to buy twice as many stamps as she bought the previous year. How many stamps will Wendy have in her collection after 15 years?

    A. 16,384
    B. 32,767
    C. 32,768
    D. 65,534

13. In the space provided below, evaluate the following series. Show your work.

    $$\sum_{k=1}^{48} [2 - 5(k + 2)]$$

© 2002 Buckle Down Publishing Company. DO NOT DUPLICATE.

14. This table shows the cost of buying different numbers of pairs of jeans.

Pairs of Jeans

Number of Pairs	1	2	3	4
Total Cost	$14.99	$28.98	$41.97	$53.96

Which is the best prediction for the cost of 9 pairs of jeans?

A. $98.91
B. $99.91
C. $101.91
D. $102.91

15. Margaret is looking for a long distance phone company. She has found four companies that she likes. Here is what each company offers.

Long Distance Companies' Monthly Charges

A	B	C	D
$39.45 unlimited calls	$14.99 + $0.95 per call	$10.99 + $1.09 per call	$29.95 0–24 calls per month OR $48.95 25+ calls per month

Based on finances alone, which company should Margaret decide to go with if she plans on making an average of 25 calls a month?

A. Company A
B. Company B
C. Company C
D. Company D

© 2002 Buckle Down Publishing Company. DO NOT DUPLICATE.

Lesson 5: Matrices

A **matrix** is a rectangular array of numbers. Most applications of **matrices** (the plural form of **matrix**) occur in the areas of the social and physical sciences. This lesson will concentrate on the correct use of the matrix operations of addition, subtraction, and scalar multiplication.

Matrix addition

In order to add two matrices, they must be of the same **order** (have the same number of rows and columns). The sum of the matrices is a matrix of the same order. The elements of the new matrix are found by adding the corresponding elements of the original matrices.

Example

$$\begin{bmatrix} 3 & 4 & -8 \\ -8 & 1 & 0 \end{bmatrix} + \begin{bmatrix} 7 & -2 & 9 \\ -4 & -9 & 3 \end{bmatrix} = \begin{bmatrix} 3+7 & 4+(-2) & -8+9 \\ -8+(-4) & 1+(-9) & 0+3 \end{bmatrix}$$

$$= \begin{bmatrix} 10 & 2 & 1 \\ -12 & -8 & 3 \end{bmatrix}$$

Example

$$\begin{bmatrix} 5 & 8 \\ -5 & 4 \\ 9 & -4 \end{bmatrix} + \begin{bmatrix} -5 & 2 \\ 3 & 8 \\ -2 & 0 \end{bmatrix} = \begin{bmatrix} 5+(-5) & 8+2 \\ -5+3 & 4+8 \\ 9+(-2) & -4+0 \end{bmatrix}$$

$$= \begin{bmatrix} 0 & 10 \\ -2 & 12 \\ 7 & -4 \end{bmatrix}$$

 TIP: The matrices in the first example are both 2 × 3 (read "2 by 3"). The matrices in the second example are both 3 × 2 (read "3 by 2"). The elements of a matrix are identified by their position in rows and columns. In the answer to the second example, the 7 is in row 3, column 1, so its position is 3, 1.

© 2002 Buckle Down Publishing Company. DO NOT DUPLICATE.

Practice

Directions: For Numbers 1 through 4, add the matrices.

1. $\begin{bmatrix} 6 & 4 & -8 \\ -8 & 6 & -7 \\ 2 & 4 & 3 \\ 3 & -8 & -4 \end{bmatrix} + \begin{bmatrix} -4 & 6 & -2 \\ -1 & 0 & 8 \\ 8 & 4 & 8 \\ -3 & 4 & 0 \end{bmatrix} =$

2. $\begin{bmatrix} 2 & 8 & 7 & 4 \\ 9 & 8 & 4 & 2 \end{bmatrix} + \begin{bmatrix} 9 & -5 & 4 & 2 \\ -7 & 0 & 5 & 2 \end{bmatrix} =$

3. $\begin{bmatrix} -5 & 8 \\ 3 & 7 \\ 3 & 5 \\ -3 & -7 \\ 3 & 7 \end{bmatrix} + \begin{bmatrix} 6 & -4 \\ -8 & -1 \\ 8 & -1 \\ 8 & 4 \\ 8 & 4 \end{bmatrix} =$

4. $\begin{bmatrix} 2 & 8 & 7 & 4 \\ -8 & -5 & 1 & 0 \\ 9 & 8 & 2 & 7 \\ -9 & -1 & -3 & 8 \\ -2 & 4 & -5 & 3 \end{bmatrix} + \begin{bmatrix} -5 & 4 & 8 & -3 \\ 8 & 4 & -5 & 3 \\ -5 & -9 & -4 & -8 \\ 7 & 5 & -2 & 0 \\ 7 & 5 & 4 & 1 \end{bmatrix} =$

© 2002 Buckle Down Publishing Company. DO NOT DUPLICATE.

Matrix subtraction

Matrices must be of the same order to perform subtraction. When subtracting matrices, change matrix subtraction into matrix addition by following the rule of "adding the opposite." To switch from matrix subtraction to matrix addition, make the "−" a "+" and change every element of the second matrix to its opposite. (Do **not** change any elements of the first matrix.) Then follow the rule for matrix addition.

Example

$$\begin{bmatrix} 3 & 4 & -8 \\ -8 & 1 & 0 \end{bmatrix} - \begin{bmatrix} 7 & -2 & 9 \\ -4 & -9 & 3 \end{bmatrix} = \begin{bmatrix} 3 & 4 & -8 \\ -8 & 1 & 0 \end{bmatrix} + \begin{bmatrix} -7 & 2 & -9 \\ 4 & 9 & -3 \end{bmatrix}$$

$$= \begin{bmatrix} -4 & 6 & -17 \\ -4 & 10 & -3 \end{bmatrix}$$

Example

$$\begin{bmatrix} 5 & 8 \\ -5 & 4 \\ 9 & -4 \end{bmatrix} - \begin{bmatrix} -5 & 2 \\ 3 & 8 \\ -2 & 0 \end{bmatrix} = \begin{bmatrix} 5 & 8 \\ -5 & 4 \\ 9 & -4 \end{bmatrix} + \begin{bmatrix} 5 & -2 \\ -3 & -8 \\ 2 & 0 \end{bmatrix}$$

$$= \begin{bmatrix} 10 & 6 \\ -8 & -4 \\ 11 & -4 \end{bmatrix}$$

TIP: Variables can be used to name a matrix. For example, if

$$M = \begin{bmatrix} 1 & 2 \\ 3 & 4 \end{bmatrix} \text{ and } N = \begin{bmatrix} 5 & 6 \\ 7 & 8 \end{bmatrix}, \text{ then}$$

$$M + N = \begin{bmatrix} 6 & 8 \\ 10 & 12 \end{bmatrix} \text{ and } M - N = \begin{bmatrix} -4 & -4 \\ -4 & -4 \end{bmatrix}.$$

© 2002 Buckle Down Publishing Company. DO NOT DUPLICATE.

Practice

Directions: For Numbers 1 through 4, subtract the matrices.

1. $\begin{bmatrix} 6 & 4 & -8 \\ -8 & 6 & -7 \\ 2 & 4 & 3 \\ 3 & -8 & -4 \end{bmatrix} - \begin{bmatrix} -4 & 6 & -2 \\ -1 & 0 & 8 \\ 8 & 4 & 8 \\ -3 & 4 & 0 \end{bmatrix} =$

2. $\begin{bmatrix} 2 & 8 & 7 & 4 \\ 9 & 8 & 4 & 2 \end{bmatrix} - \begin{bmatrix} 9 & -5 & 4 & 2 \\ -7 & 0 & 5 & 2 \end{bmatrix} =$

3. $\begin{bmatrix} -5 & 8 \\ 3 & 7 \\ 3 & 5 \\ -3 & -7 \\ 3 & 7 \end{bmatrix} - \begin{bmatrix} 6 & -4 \\ -8 & -1 \\ 8 & -1 \\ 8 & 4 \\ 8 & 4 \end{bmatrix} =$

4. $\begin{bmatrix} 2 & 8 & 7 & 4 \\ -8 & -5 & 1 & 0 \\ 9 & 8 & 2 & 7 \\ -9 & -1 & -3 & 8 \\ -2 & 4 & -5 & 3 \end{bmatrix} - \begin{bmatrix} -5 & 4 & 8 & -3 \\ 8 & 4 & -5 & 3 \\ -5 & -9 & -4 & -8 \\ 7 & 5 & -2 & 0 \\ 7 & 5 & 4 & 1 \end{bmatrix} =$

© 2002 Buckle Down Publishing Company. DO NOT DUPLICATE.

Scalar multiplication

A **scalar** in matrix algebra is the equivalent to a constant (any real number) in basic algebra. Therefore, **scalar multiplication** means multiplying a matrix by a real number. The result is a matrix of the same order as the original, formed by multiplying each element of the original by the scalar.

Example

$$6 \begin{bmatrix} 3 & -8 & 7 \\ 8 & 4 & -2 \\ -1 & 5 & 0 \end{bmatrix} = \begin{bmatrix} \mathbf{6} \cdot 3 & \mathbf{6} \cdot (-8) & \mathbf{6} \cdot 7 \\ \mathbf{6} \cdot 8 & \mathbf{6} \cdot 4 & \mathbf{6} \cdot (-2) \\ \mathbf{6} \cdot (-1) & \mathbf{6} \cdot 5 & \mathbf{6} \cdot 0 \end{bmatrix}$$

$$= \begin{bmatrix} 18 & -48 & 42 \\ 48 & 24 & -12 \\ -6 & 30 & 0 \end{bmatrix}$$

Example

$$-2 \begin{bmatrix} 5 & 8 \\ -2 & -7 \\ -3 & 1 \\ -8 & 4 \\ 6 & -5 \\ 2 & 0 \end{bmatrix} = \begin{bmatrix} \mathbf{-2} \cdot 5 & \mathbf{-2} \cdot 8 \\ \mathbf{-2} \cdot (-2) & \mathbf{-2} \cdot (-7) \\ \mathbf{-2} \cdot (-3) & \mathbf{-2} \cdot 1 \\ \mathbf{-2} \cdot (-8) & \mathbf{-2} \cdot 4 \\ \mathbf{-2} \cdot 6 & \mathbf{-2} \cdot (-5) \\ \mathbf{-2} \cdot 2 & \mathbf{-2} \cdot 0 \end{bmatrix}$$

$$= \begin{bmatrix} -10 & -16 \\ 4 & 14 \\ 6 & -2 \\ 16 & -8 \\ -12 & 10 \\ -4 & 0 \end{bmatrix}$$

TIP: If $P = \begin{bmatrix} 1 & 2 \\ 3 & 4 \end{bmatrix}$, then $3P = \begin{bmatrix} 3 & 6 \\ 9 & 12 \end{bmatrix}$.

© 2002 Buckle Down Publishing Company. DO NOT DUPLICATE.

Practice

Directions: For Numbers 1 through 4, multiply to find the scalar product.

1.
$$5 \begin{bmatrix} 8 & -5 & 3 & -4 & 9 \\ -2 & 5 & -7 & -4 & 0 \end{bmatrix} =$$

2.
$$-7 \begin{bmatrix} 5 & -7 & 6 & 3 & -4 & -8 \\ 4 & -5 & 2 & -1 & 1 & 2 \\ 3 & -2 & 4 & -8 & -2 & -3 \\ 5 & -4 & -8 & 10 & -14 & 2 \end{bmatrix} =$$

3.
$$-9 \begin{bmatrix} 2 & -4 & -3 \\ 2 & 0 & 4 \\ 1 & -8 & -9 \\ 0 & -8 & -4 \\ -8 & -4 & 2 \\ -1 & 4 & 8 \end{bmatrix} =$$

4.
$$0 \begin{bmatrix} 5 & 6 & 4 \\ 1 & -8 & -4 \\ 257 & 368 & -485 \end{bmatrix} =$$

 TIP: The matrix formed in Number 4 is called the **zero matrix**. Any matrix in which all the elements are zero is called a zero matrix.

© 2002 Buckle Down Publishing Company. DO NOT DUPLICATE.

Applications of Matrices

Matrices can be useful for organizing numbers in real-world situations.

Example

Tyler, Emily, Libby, and Daniel each made $7 an hour working at the car wash during summer vacation. The following matrix shows the number of hours each worked in June, July, and August.

Hours Worked

	Tyler	Emily	Libby	Daniel
June	116	106	98	125
July	124	108	110	85
August	96	99	93	101

Represent in a matrix the amount of money each earned in June, July, and August. (Multiply the matrix above by 7.)

$$7\begin{bmatrix} 116 & 106 & 98 & 125 \\ 124 & 108 & 110 & 85 \\ 96 & 99 & 93 & 101 \end{bmatrix} = \begin{bmatrix} 812 & 742 & 686 & 875 \\ 868 & 756 & 770 & 595 \\ 672 & 693 & 651 & 707 \end{bmatrix}$$

The following matrix shows the amounts of money that Tyler, Emily, Libby, and Daniel earned in June, July, and August.

Money Earned (in dollars)

	Tyler	Emily	Libby	Daniel
June	812	742	686	875
July	868	756	770	595
August	672	693	651	707

© 2002 Buckle Down Publishing Company. DO NOT DUPLICATE.

© 2002 Buckle Down Publishing Company. DO NOT DUPLICATE.

Practice

Directions: Use the following information to answer Numbers 1 through 3.

A sporting-goods store sells football jerseys in three different colors and four different sizes. The store makes $25 for each jersey it sells. The numbers of jerseys sold are represented in the following matrices.

Jerseys Sold in October

	S	M	L	XL
Burgundy	36	39	72	62
Gold	41	25	65	40
White	17	30	47	58

Jerseys Sold in November

	S	M	L	XL
Burgundy	35	51	56	74
Gold	36	38	47	55
White	24	22	40	63

1. Represent in a matrix the number of each size and color jersey sold in October and November combined.

2. Represent in a matrix the amount of money the store made selling each size and color jersey in October.

3. How much money did the store make selling jerseys for the entire month of November?

Directions: Use the following information to answer Numbers 4 through 6.

A department store has posted its sales (in thousands of dollars) from four of their departments in three different cities for 2000 and 2001. The sales are represented in the following matrices.

Sales for 2000
(in thousands of dollars)

	Madison	Des Moines	Springfield
Electronics	104	78	83
Sporting Goods	112	98	103
Housewares	54	31	22
Lawn and Garden	9	12	18

Sales for 2001
(in thousands of dollars)

	Madison	Des Moines	Springfield
Electronics	114	89	81
Sporting Goods	103	113	108
Housewares	52	35	25
Lawn and Garden	12	9	16

4. Represent in a matrix the combined sales for each department in each city for 2000 and 2001.

5. Represent in a matrix the change of sales for each department in each city from 2000 to 2001.

6. Represent in a matrix the amount of money that each department in each city donated to charity in 2001 if 5% of sales is donated to charity.

© 2002 Buckle Down Publishing Company. DO NOT DUPLICATE.

Buckle Down!®

Book 2

Form A

on Algebra I

This test belongs to: _____

Confidence Corner™

Sample Questions to Illustrate the Difference in Confidence Levels

1. If Superman flew to the North Pole from New York City, which direction would he be flying?

   Confidence Corner™ 5 4 3 2 1

   A. North
   B. East
   C. South
   D. West

2. If Superman picked up the Washington Monument, how many tons would he be lifting?

   Confidence Corner™ 5 4 3 2 1

   A. 89,000
   B. 91,000
   C. 94,000
   D. 101,000

Finding Terms of a Sequence

Type	Recursive	Explicit
Arithmetic	a_1 $a_n = (a_{n-1}) + d$ for $n > 1$	$a_n = a_1 + (n-1)d$
Geometric	a_1 $a_n = (a_{n-1})r$ for $r > 1$	$a_n = a_1 r^{(n-1)}$

Evaluating a Series

Type	Formula
Arithmetic	$S_n = \dfrac{n(a_1 + a_n)}{2}$
Geometric	$S_n = \dfrac{a_1(1 - r^n)}{1 - r}$ If $r = 1$, then $S_n = na_1$

ISBN 0-7836-2613-4

Catalog #BD US10A2 3   4 5 6 7 8 9 10

Copyright © 2002 by Buckle Down Publishing Company. All rights reserved. No part of this work may be reproduced or transmitted in any form or by any means, electronic or mechanical, including photocopying, recording, or any information storage or retrieval systems, except as may be expressly permitted in writing by the publisher, Buckle Down Publishing Company, P.O. Box 2180, Iowa City, IA 52244-2180.

Cover image: © Corbis

1. Jake wants to demonstrate the relationship between his quiz scores and the number of hours he studies each night. What type of graph would **best** display Jake's data?

   A. bar graph
   B. scatterplot
   C. circle graph
   D. box-and-whisker plot

2. Simplify:

   $$\sqrt[3]{-27x^3y^9z^{18}}$$

   A. $-3xy^6z^{15}$
   B. $-3xy^3z^6$
   C. $3xy^6z^{15}$
   D. $3xy^3z^6$

3. Completely factor:

   $$6x^2 - 5x - 25$$

   A. $(3x + 5)(2x - 5)$
   B. $(3x - 5)(2x + 5)$
   C. $(x - 5)(6x + 5)$
   D. $(x + 5)(6x - 5)$

4. Subtract:

   $$\begin{bmatrix} 6 & -2 & -7 \\ 8 & 4 & -6 \\ 3 & -9 & 0 \end{bmatrix} - \begin{bmatrix} 4 & 5 & 1 \\ -8 & 3 & 0 \\ -7 & 2 & -9 \end{bmatrix}$$

   A. $\begin{bmatrix} 2 & -7 & -8 \\ 16 & 1 & -6 \\ 10 & -11 & 9 \end{bmatrix}$

   B. $\begin{bmatrix} 2 & 3 & -8 \\ 0 & 7 & -6 \\ -4 & -7 & -9 \end{bmatrix}$

   C. $\begin{bmatrix} 10 & 3 & -6 \\ 0 & 7 & -6 \\ -4 & -7 & -9 \end{bmatrix}$

   D. $\begin{bmatrix} 10 & -7 & -6 \\ 16 & 1 & -6 \\ 10 & -11 & 9 \end{bmatrix}$

Confidence Corner™ 5 4 3 2 1

© 2002 Buckle Down Publishing Company. DO NOT DUPLICATE.

GO ON

5. In the space provided below, add the rational expressions.

☐ $\dfrac{x-2}{x+5} + \dfrac{x-4}{x-3}$

© 2002 Buckle Down Publishing Company. DO NOT DUPLICATE.

6. A penny, nickel, dime, and quarter are all tossed into the air at the same time. What is the probability that all four coins will land tails up?

A. $\frac{1}{16}$

B. $\frac{1}{2}$

C. $\frac{7}{8}$

D. $\frac{15}{16}$

7. Albert is doing a science experiment with an unknown substance. He is testing how long it takes for the substance to react with oxygen. His results are shown in the following table.

Amount of Substance (in ounces)	1	2	3	4	5	6
Reaction Time (in minutes)	1	6	12	19	27	?

If the relationship between the amount of substance and the reaction time continues to change as it has, how long will it take for 6 ounces of the substance to react?

A. 36 minutes

B. 35 minutes

C. 34 minutes

D. 33 minutes

Directions: For Numbers 8 and 9, use the following information.

Mr. Pauly made the following stem-and-leaf plot to show the test scores that his students received on the history midterm.

Midterm Scores

5	6 8
6	1 4 7
7	0 3 6 8 8
8	2 2 4 9 9 9
9	1 1 3 4 5
10	0

8. How many students scored between 75 and 85?

A. 2

B. 5

C. 6

D. 11

9. What is the mode of the scores?

A. 80

B. 82

C. 89

D. 91

© 2002 Buckle Down Publishing Company. DO NOT DUPLICATE.

GO ON

10. Simplify:

$$(5a^3b^4cd^2)^3$$

A. $15a^6b^7c^4d^5$

B. $15a^9b^{12}c^3d^6$

C. $125a^6b^7c^4d^5$

D. $125a^9b^{12}c^3d^6$

11. Mark has a rectangular storage shed that is 10 ft by 15 ft. He is building an addition that will add the same amount to both the length and the width, as shown below. The area of the shed with the addition will be 500 ft^2.

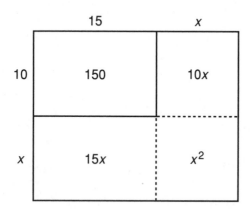

How many feet is Mark adding to both the length and the width?

A. 10 ft

B. 12 ft

C. 14 ft

D. 16 ft

12. Which type of correlation does the following scatterplot represent?

A. no correlation

B. perfect correlation

C. positive correlation

D. negative correlation

13. A local pizza restaurant offers 2 choices of crust, 3 choices of cheese, 4 choices of vegetables, and 5 choices of meat. How many different pizzas can be made if each pizza uses one type of crust, cheese, vegetable, and meat?

A. 14

B. 60

C. 96

D. 120

© 2002 Buckle Down Publishing Company. DO NOT DUPLICATE.

GO ON

Directions: Use the following information to answer Numbers 14 through 16.

The Environmental Club at Johnson High School asked 13 students how many aluminum cans their families recycled each week. The following list shows the data that was collected.

0, 2, 2, 5, 6, 8, 9, 10, 10, 10, 11, 14, 30

14. What is the median?

A. 8
B. 9
C. 10
D. 11

15. What is the range?

A. 10
B. 14
C. 28
D. 30

16. In the space provided below, find the mean.

© 2002 Buckle Down Publishing Company. DO NOT DUPLICATE.

GO ON

17. Toshanda has worked the last four years at the swimming pool as a lifeguard. She earned $3,060 the first year and received an increase in pay of 4% each of the following three years. In the space provided below, use the formula for evaluating a geometric series to find the total amount of money that Toshanda has earned while working at the swimming pool.

© 2002 Buckle Down Publishing Company. DO NOT DUPLICATE.

Directions: For Numbers 18 through 20, use the following information.

The student council at Washington High School consists of members with the following ages.

14, 18, 17, 15, 15, 16, 17, 18,
14, 14, 15, 16, 16, 17, 18, 16,
16, 17, 18, 15, 18, 16, 16, 15

One person is chosen each week to read the minutes from the student council meeting on the news portion of the Broadcasting Class's weekly TV show.

18. What is $P(15)$ (the person chosen to read the minutes this week is 15)?

A. $\frac{1}{3}$

B. $\frac{7}{24}$

C. $\frac{1}{4}$

D. $\frac{5}{24}$

19. What is $P(18')$?

A. $\frac{5}{24}$

B. $\frac{1}{4}$

C. $\frac{19}{24}$

D. $\frac{5}{6}$

20. What is $P(14 \text{ or } 16)$?

A. $\frac{5}{12}$

B. $\frac{11}{24}$

C. $\frac{1}{2}$

D. $\frac{13}{24}$

21. Completely factor:

$$9x^2 - 100$$

A. $(x - 25)(9x + 4)$

B. $(3x + 2)(3x - 50)$

C. $(9x + 1)(x - 100)$

D. $(3x + 10)(3x - 10)$

22. Nichole has two number cubes. Each cube has sides numbered 1 through 6. Nichole is going to roll each cube once and add the numbers that appear on the top of the cubes. What is the sample space?

A. {1, 2}

B. {1, 2, 3, 4, 5, 6}

C. {2, 3, 4, 5, 6, 7, 8, 9, 10, 11, 12}

D. {1, 2, 3, 4, 5, 6, 7, 8, 9, 10, 11, 12}

23. What is the 120th term of the following sequence?

$$-3, -1, 1, 3, 5, \ldots$$

A. 117

B. 232

C. 235

D. 240

© 2002 Buckle Down Publishing Company. DO NOT DUPLICATE.

GO ON

24. Gloria added on to three sides of a cement patio that was 12 ft by 18 ft, as shown below.

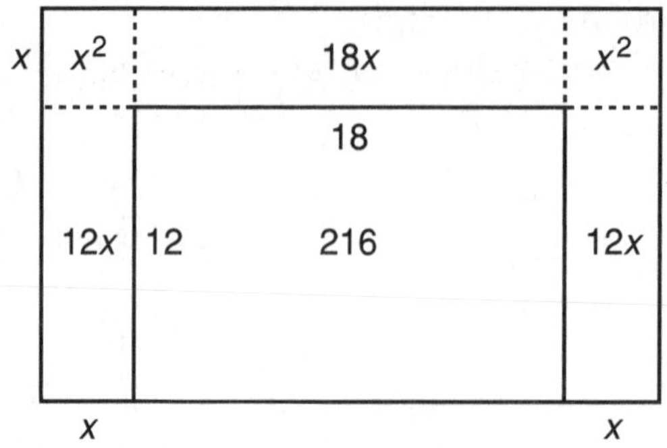

x	x^2	$18x$	x^2
		18	
	12		
$12x$		216	$12x$
	x		x

The total area of the patio is now 416 ft². In the space provided below, find the new dimensions of the patio.

© 2002 Buckle Down Publishing Company. DO NOT DUPLICATE.

GO ON

Confidence Corner™ 5 4 3 2 1

25. The Bedford Election Committee released the following histogram of information to show the percentage of registered voters, by age group, who voted in Bedford's mayoral election.

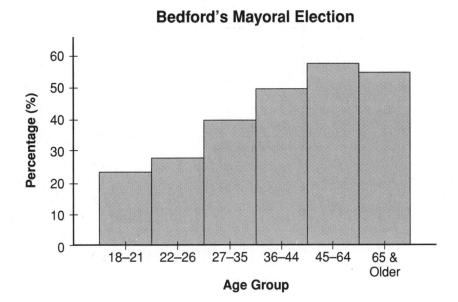

Bedford's Mayoral Election

Which conclusion is supported by the information from the histogram?

A. About 40% of people in Bedford aged 27–35 voted.

B. Most 18–21-year-olds in Bedford are not registered voters.

C. The 45–64 age group has the most registered voters in Bedford.

D. Over half of Bedford's registered voters 65 and older voted in the election.

Confidence Corner™ 5 4 3 2 1

26. Patrick's mom wants to reward him for every "A" he gets on his report card. He has two options from which to choose.

Option A—$10 for every "A"

Option B—$1 for the first "A," plus $2 for the second "A," plus $4 for the third "A," and so on, doubling with each "A"

What is the **least** number of "A's" that Patrick must receive to make Option B the better option?

A. 3

B. 4

C. 5

D. 6

© 2002 Buckle Down Publishing Company. DO NOT DUPLICATE.

GO ON

27. Evaluate:

$$\sum_{n=0}^{10} (5 \cdot 2^n)$$

A. 5,115

B. 10,235

C. 20,470

D. 25,625

28. Divide:

$$\frac{2x^2 - 5x - 3}{x^2 - 9} \div \frac{6x^2 - x - 2}{x^2 - 4x - 21}$$

A. $\frac{x - 7}{2x + 1}$

B. $\frac{x - 3}{x + 3}$

C. $\frac{2x + 1}{x - 3}$

D. $\frac{x - 7}{3x - 2}$

29. Multiply:

$$(4x^2y^3z)(-8xy^5z^2)$$

A. $-32x^2y^{15}z^2$

B. $-32x^3y^8z^3$

C. $-4x^2y^{15}z^2$

D. $-4x^3y^8z^3$

30. Solve:

$$4x^2 - 10 = -3x$$

A. $x = -3$ and $x = \frac{3}{2}$

B. $x = -2$ and $x = \frac{5}{4}$

C. $x = \frac{7}{6}$ and $x = 1$

D. $x = \frac{1}{3}$ and $x = 8$

31. The manager of Mega-Theatres is presenting a sales report. She made the following line graph to show that ticket sales have increased since she was hired.

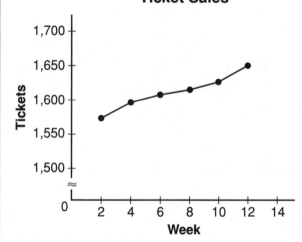

Ticket Sales

If the trend continues, what is the **best** prediction for the number of tickets that will be sold in week 14?

A. 1,575

B. 1,620

C. 1,665

D. 1,725

© 2002 Buckle Down Publishing Company. DO NOT DUPLICATE.

GO ON

32. The following matrices show the numbers of different kinds of hits that four
players got during the first half and the second half of the baseball season.

	1st-Half Hits			
	Rich	Juan	Bobby	Ryan
Single	120	102	89	93
Double	24	10	24	22
Triple	4	3	1	4
Home Run	12	1	17	17

	2nd-Half Hits			
	Rich	Juan	Bobby	Ryan
Single	86	100	81	61
Double	13	16	24	12
Triple	1	8	3	2
Home Run	25	1	14	13

In the space provided below, represent in a matrix the total number of each
kind of hit the players got for the entire season.

© 2002 Buckle Down Publishing Company. DO NOT DUPLICATE.

GO ON ➤

33. Completely factor:

$$6x^4 + 8x^3 - 10x^2$$

  A. $2x^2(3x^2 + 4x - 5)$

  B. $4x(3x^2 - 2)(x + 5)$

  C. $2x^2(3x + 2)(x - 5)$

  D. $4x(3x^3 + 4x^2 - 5x)$

34. The population of a certain species of bacterium increases by 5% every hour. If there are 50 bacteria present in the population after one hour ($a_1 = 50$), what is the population of bacteria after 10 hours? (Round your answer to the nearest hundredth.)

  A. 75.45

  B. 77.57

  C. 81.44

  D. 85.52

35. Evaluate:

$$\sum_{n=1}^{9} (3 - 5n)$$

  A. -198

  B. -156

  C. 156

  D. 198

36. Multiply to find the scalar product:

$$-3 \begin{bmatrix} 4 & -2 & 6 \\ -3 & 1 & -5 \\ 8 & 0 & 9 \end{bmatrix}$$

  A. $\begin{bmatrix} 1 & -5 & 3 \\ -6 & -2 & -8 \\ 5 & -3 & 6 \end{bmatrix}$

  B. $\begin{bmatrix} -12 & 6 & -18 \\ 9 & -3 & 15 \\ -24 & 0 & -27 \end{bmatrix}$

  C. $\begin{bmatrix} 1 & 5 & -3 \\ 6 & 2 & -8 \\ -5 & -3 & 6 \end{bmatrix}$

  D. $\begin{bmatrix} 12 & -6 & 18 \\ -9 & -3 & -15 \\ 24 & 0 & 27 \end{bmatrix}$

© 2002 Buckle Down Publishing Company. DO NOT DUPLICATE.

GO ON

37. Mr. Boolean's students received the following scores on the algebra midterm.

75, 81, 81, 84, 86, 86, 87, 87, 88, 89, 89, 90, 90, 92, 95, 98, 99, 99, 100, 100

In the space provided below, construct a box-and-whisker plot that represents this data.

© 2002 Buckle Down Publishing Company. DO NOT DUPLICATE.

GO ON

38. Roy prepared the following graph for his boss to strengthen his position that he deserves a raise.

Salary History

What did Roy **most likely** want his boss to interpret from the graph?

A. Roy has been working at the company for a very long time.
B. Roy's responsibilities have increased more than his salary has.
C. Roy's salary increases have not kept up with the rate of inflation.
D. There has been very little change in Roy's salary over the 25 years.

39. In the space provided below, multiply the polynomials.

$(3x + 7)(2x^2 + 4x - 5)$

© 2002 Buckle Down Publishing Company. DO NOT DUPLICATE.

GO ON

40. Completely factor:

$$x^2 - 12x + 20$$

A. $(x + 5)(x + 4)$
B. $(x - 5)(x - 4)$
C. $(x - 2)(x - 10)$
D. $(x + 1)(x + 20)$

41. Darcy rolled a cube numbered 1 through 6 a number of times. Each time she rolled the cube, she recorded the number on the top. She displayed her results in this frequency chart.

Number	Tally Marks	Frequency
1	IIII	4
2	III	3
3	JHT II	7
4	JHT I	6
5	III	3
6	JHT II	7

What is Darcy's experimental probability of rolling a 4 [Exp $P(4)$]?

A. $\frac{1}{3}$

B. $\frac{1}{4}$

C. $\frac{1}{5}$

D. $\frac{1}{6}$

42. The following table shows the amounts of money Jim had in his bank account for four weeks.

Week	Amount
1	$200
2	$195
3	$190
4	$185

If Jim continues to withdraw money at the same rate each week without making a deposit, how much money will Jim have in his account in week 20?

A. $100
B. $105
C. $110
D. $115

43. Completely factor:

$$4x^3 + 14x^2 - 30x$$

A. $(4x^2 - 15x)(x + 2)$
B. $(2x + 3)(2x^2 - 10)$
C. $2x(x + 5)(2x - 3)$
D. $4x^2(2x + 6)(x - 5)$

44. What is the LCD of $\frac{x^2 + 2x - 3}{x^2 + 2x - 8}$ and $\frac{x^2 + 6x + 5}{x^2 - 16}$?

A. $(x + 3)(x - 2)(x + 5)$
B. $(x + 1)(x - 8)(x - 4)$
C. $(x + 4)(x - 4)(x - 2)$
D. $(x + 3)(x - 1)(x - 5)$

© 2002 Buckle Down Publishing Company. DO NOT DUPLICATE.

GO ON

45. A rectangular house sits on a rectangular lot as shown below. The length of the house is five feet more than the width. The length of the lot is twice the length of the house. The width of the lot is three times the width of the house.

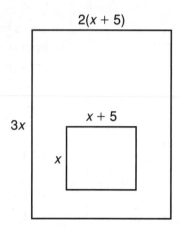

In the space provided below, find the polynomial that represents the area of the lot that is not covered by the house.

© 2002 Buckle Down Publishing Company. DO NOT DUPLICATE.

GO ON ▶

46. What is the GCF of $6x^2y^3$ and $8x^5y^2$?

    A. $24x^5y^3$

    B. $24x^2y^2$

    C. $2x^5y^3$

    D. $2x^2y^2$

47. Simplify:

    $$(3x^{-2}y^4z^{-6})^{-2}$$

    A. $\dfrac{x^4z^{12}}{9y^8}$

    B. $\dfrac{9y^8}{x^4z^{12}}$

    C. $-\dfrac{6x^2z^8}{y^6}$

    D. $-\dfrac{z^8}{6x^2y^6}$

48. Completely factor:

    $$x^2 - 5x - 36$$

    A. $(x + 6)(x - 6)$

    B. $(x - 9)(x + 4)$

    C. $(x - 2)(x + 18)$

    D. $(x - 3)(x + 12)$

49. Two jars are on the kitchen counter. One jar contains 6 red and 8 green gumballs. The other jar contains 5 pink and 9 white mints. Sara took one gumball and one mint from the jars without looking. In the space provided below, find the probability that Sara took a green gumball and a white mint.

© 2002 Buckle Down Publishing Company. DO NOT DUPLICATE.

50. In the space provided below, completely factor the trinomial.

☐ $20x^2 - 6x - 2$

© 2002 Buckle Down Publishing Company. DO NOT DUPLICATE.

	Confidence Level	Number of Items	Confidence Points
Correct	1	× _____ =	_____
	2	× _____ =	_____
	3	× _____ =	_____
	4	× _____ =	_____
	5	× _____ =	_____
	Subtotal		+ _____
Incorrect	−1	× _____ =	− _____
	−2	× _____ =	− _____
	−3	× _____ =	− _____
	−4	× _____ =	− _____
	−5	× _____ =	− _____
	Subtotal		− _____
	TOTAL	Number of Multiple-Choice Items **40**	Confidence Score _____

Negative Scores (Incorrect)					Positive Scores (Correct)					Confidence Level
⁻5	⁻4	⁻3	⁻2	⁻1	⁺5	⁺4	⁺3	⁺2	⁺1	
1	1	1	1	1	1	1	1	1	1	
2	2	2	2	2	2	2	2	2	2	
3	3	3	3	3	3	3	3	3	3	
4	4	4	4	4	4	4	4	4	4	
5	5	5	5	5	5	5	5	5	5	
6	6	6	6	6	6	6	6	6	6	
7	7	7	7	7	7	7	7	7	7	
8	8	8	8	8	8	8	8	8	8	
9	9	9	9	9	9	9	9	9	9	
10	10	10	10	10	10	10	10	10	10	
11	11	11	11	11	11	11	11	11	11	
12	12	12	12	12	12	12	12	12	12	
13	13	13	13	13	13	13	13	13	13	
14	14	14	14	14	14	14	14	14	14	
15	15	15	15	15	15	15	15	15	15	
16	16	16	16	16	16	16	16	16	16	Test Questions
17	17	17	17	17	17	17	17	17	17	
18	18	18	18	18	18	18	18	18	18	
19	19	19	19	19	19	19	19	19	19	
20	20	20	20	20	20	20	20	20	20	
21	21	21	21	21	21	21	21	21	21	
22	22	22	22	22	22	22	22	22	22	
23	23	23	23	23	23	23	23	23	23	
24	24	24	24	24	24	24	24	24	24	
25	25	25	25	25	25	25	25	25	25	
26	26	26	26	26	26	26	26	26	26	
27	27	27	27	27	27	27	27	27	27	
28	28	28	28	28	28	28	28	28	28	
29	29	29	29	29	29	29	29	29	29	
30	30	30	30	30	30	30	30	30	30	
31	31	31	31	31	31	31	31	31	31	
32	32	32	32	32	32	32	32	32	32	
33	33	33	33	33	33	33	33	33	33	
34	34	34	34	34	34	34	34	34	34	
35	35	35	35	35	35	35	35	35	35	
36	36	36	36	36	36	36	36	36	36	
37	37	37	37	37	37	37	37	37	37	
38	38	38	38	38	38	38	38	38	38	
39	39	39	39	39	39	39	39	39	39	
40	40	40	40	40	40	40	40	40	40	
41	41	41	41	41	41	41	41	41	41	
42	42	42	42	42	42	42	42	42	42	
43	43	43	43	43	43	43	43	43	43	
44	44	44	44	44	44	44	44	44	44	
45	45	45	45	45	45	45	45	45	45	
46	46	46	46	46	46	46	46	46	46	
47	47	47	47	47	47	47	47	47	47	
48	48	48	48	48	48	48	48	48	48	
49	49	49	49	49	49	49	49	49	49	
50	50	50	50	50	50	50	50	50	50	

© 2002 Buckle Down Publishing Company. DO NOT DUPLICATE.

Algebra I, Book 2 Diagnostic Test
Self-Scoring Guide

Name: _____

Directions:

1. Remove this self-scoring guide from your test booklet and write your name on it.

2. For each multiple-choice item you answered correctly, fill in the circle next to the item number below. Each of these items is worth 1 point.

3. For each item you answered incorrectly, leave the circle blank.

4. Your teacher will score the open-response items. Record the points (0–2) you received for each item in the box next to the item number below.

5. Find your total points scored in each unit. Then mark the column showing the range of points you earned in each unit.

6. Identify the categories you need to review and study those sections in *Buckle Down on Algebra I, Book 2*. Your teacher can direct you to specific reviews related to each item.

Unit	Item Number				Range of Points		
					Below Average	**Average**	**Excellent**
1. Analytical Thinking	2 ○ 3 ○ 4 ○ 5 ☐ 7 ○ 10 ○ 11 ○ 17 ☐ 21 ○ 23 ○ 24 ☐ 26 ○ 27 ○ 28 ○ 29 ○ 30 ○ 32 ☐ 33 ○ 34 ○ 35 ○ 36 ○ 39 ☐ 40 ○ 42 ○ 43 ○ 44 ○ 45 ☐ 46 ○ 47 ○ 48 ○ 50 ☐				0–19	20–28	29–38
2. Data and Probability	1 ○ 6 ○ 8 ○ 9 ○ 12 ○ 13 ○ 14 ○ 15 ○ 16 ☐ 18 ○ 19 ○ 20 ○ 22 ○ 25 ○ 31 ○ 37 ☐ 38 ○ 41 ○ 49 ☐				0–11	12–16	17–22

Points	Recommended Study
Excellent	General review of key concepts
Average	Review of key concepts and targeted study areas
Below Average	Intense review of ALL targeted study areas

Cut or tear carefully along this line.

© 2002 Buckle Down Publishing Company. DO NOT DUPLICATE.

PUBLISHING COMPANY

Catalog #BD US10A2 3

ISBN 0-7836-2613-4

Test Your Skills

1. Add:

$$\begin{bmatrix} 24 & -9 \\ -20 & 28 \\ 88 & 10 \end{bmatrix} + \begin{bmatrix} -1 & -18 \\ 8 & 40 \\ -19 & -99 \end{bmatrix}$$

A. $\begin{bmatrix} 25 & 27 \\ 28 & 68 \\ 107 & 109 \end{bmatrix}$

B. $\begin{bmatrix} 23 & 27 \\ -28 & 68 \\ 67 & -89 \end{bmatrix}$

C. $\begin{bmatrix} 25 & -9 \\ -28 & 68 \\ 107 & 109 \end{bmatrix}$

D. $\begin{bmatrix} 23 & -27 \\ -12 & 68 \\ 69 & -89 \end{bmatrix}$

2. In the space provided below, represent in a matrix the difference of the two matrices.

$$\begin{bmatrix} 3 & -6 & 4 & -2 \\ 9 & -3 & 7 & -5 \end{bmatrix} - \begin{bmatrix} 14 & -8 & 0 & 6 \\ -3 & -22 & 4 & 9 \end{bmatrix}$$

3. Multiply:

$$4 \begin{bmatrix} -3 & -5 & -6 \\ 4 & 10 & -8 \\ 2 & 0.5 & 0.6 \end{bmatrix}$$

A. $\begin{bmatrix} 1 & -1 & -2 \\ 0 & 14 & -4 \\ 6 & 4.5 & 4.6 \end{bmatrix}$

B. $\begin{bmatrix} -12 & -20 & -24 \\ 16 & 40 & -32 \\ 8 & 2 & 2.4 \end{bmatrix}$

C. $\begin{bmatrix} 12 & 20 & 24 \\ 16 & 40 & 32 \\ 8 & 2 & 2.4 \end{bmatrix}$

D. $\begin{bmatrix} 7 & 9 & 10 \\ 0 & -6 & 12 \\ 2 & 3.5 & 3.4 \end{bmatrix}$

4. In the space provided below, represent in a matrix the scalar product.

$$3 \begin{bmatrix} 14 & 15 & 40 \\ -7 & 31 & -19 \\ 25 & -1 & -4 \end{bmatrix}$$

© 2002 Buckle Down Publishing Company. DO NOT DUPLICATE.

5. The following matrices show the number of tickets that were sold for *Albert Algebra* at the theater on opening weekend.

Tickets Sold Saturday

	1:00	4:00	7:00
Adult	261	320	476
Child	386	342	204
Senior	103	88	67

Tickets Sold Sunday

	1:00	4:00	7:00
Adult	220	236	536
Child	355	416	159
Senior	172	98	55

In the space provided below, represent in a matrix the number of adult, child, and senior tickets that were sold for each showtime on Saturday and Sunday combined.

6. Subtract:

$$\begin{bmatrix} 6 & 72 & 28 \\ -18 & 15 & 64 \\ 45 & -11 & 40 \\ 30 & -7 & -92 \end{bmatrix} - \begin{bmatrix} -84 & 0 & -33 \\ 62 & -8 & -2 \\ 25 & 55 & 40 \\ -40 & 16 & -12 \end{bmatrix}$$

A. $\begin{bmatrix} 90 & 72 & 61 \\ -80 & 23 & 66 \\ 20 & -66 & 0 \\ 70 & -23 & -80 \end{bmatrix}$

B. $\begin{bmatrix} -78 & 72 & -5 \\ -44 & 7 & 62 \\ 20 & -44 & 0 \\ -10 & 9 & 80 \end{bmatrix}$

C. $\begin{bmatrix} -78 & 72 & -5 \\ 44 & 7 & 62 \\ 70 & 44 & 80 \\ -10 & 9 & -104 \end{bmatrix}$

D. $\begin{bmatrix} 90 & 72 & 61 \\ 80 & 23 & 66 \\ 70 & 66 & 80 \\ 70 & 23 & 104 \end{bmatrix}$

© 2002 Buckle Down Publishing Company. DO NOT DUPLICATE.

Unit 2

Data and Probability

Newspapers and magazines frequently use graphs to present some aspect of the news, such as how the government is spending tax dollars or how the season's top movies compare at the box office. Meteorologists give the chance of precipitation as a probability in the form of a percent.

In this unit, you will find the measures of central tendency (mean, median, and mode) and the range of data sets. You will interpret, analyze, and display data in the form of tables, charts, graphs, and plots. You will also represent the outcomes for a given situation and calculate the probability that an event will or will not occur.

In This Unit

Statistics

Displaying Data

Probability

© 2002 Buckle Down Publishing Company. DO NOT DUPLICATE.

Lesson 6: Statistics

Statistics is a set of methods used to collect, organize, describe, and analyze numerical data.

Measures of Central Tendency

A **measure of central tendency** uses one number to represent the center of all the values in a data set. This number is a value around which all the values in a data set tend to cluster. The measures of central tendency are the **mean**, **median**, and **mode**.

Mean

The **mean** is the arithmetic **average** of the values in a data set. The mean can be found by adding all the values in a data set and dividing by the number of values in that data set.

Median

The **median** is the **middle** value in a data set arranged in increasing or decreasing order. If the number of data values is odd, the median is the value in the middle of the list. If the number of data values is even, the median is the average of the middle two values.

Mode

The **mode** is the value that appears **most often** in a data set. In a set of values, there may be one mode, more than one mode (if two or more values appear most often), or no mode at all (if all the values are different).

 TIP: Sometimes there is a data value that is noticeably larger or smaller than the rest of the data values. An extreme value like this is called an **outlier**. A single outlier can have an effect on the mean, but will not affect the median or the mode. Outliers are often viewed as possible errors or flukes in the data.

© 2002 Buckle Down Publishing Company. DO NOT DUPLICATE.

Example

The following list of numbers represents the number of interceptions Brett threw in his first nine complete seasons as a quarterback.

13, 24, 14, 13, 13, 16, 23, 23, 16

Find the mean, median, and mode of these numbers.

Arrange the numbers in order from least to greatest.

13, 13, 13, 14, 16, 16, 23, 23, 24

mean: $\dfrac{13 + 13 + 13 + 14 + 16 + 16 + 23 + 23 + 24}{9} = \dfrac{155}{9} = 17.\overline{2}$

median: 16

mode: 13

The mean is $17.\overline{2}$, the median is 16, and the mode is 13.

Example

Find the mean, median, and mode of this set of test scores.

Miss Mary Mack's Class

Student	1	2	3	4	5	6	7	8
Score	69	82	79	82	70	70	85	87

Arrange the scores in order from least to greatest.

69, 70, 70, 79, 82, 82, 85, 87

mean: $\dfrac{69 + 70 + 70 + 79 + 82 + 82 + 85 + 87}{8} = \dfrac{624}{8} = 78$

median: $\dfrac{79 + 82}{2} = \dfrac{161}{2} = 80.5$

mode: 70 and 82

The mean is 78, the median is 80.5, and the modes are 70 and 82.

© 2002 Buckle Down Publishing Company. DO NOT DUPLICATE.

Practice

Directions: Use the following table to answer Numbers 1 through 5.

Bill's Bowling Scores

Game	1	2	3	4	5	6	7	8	9	10
Score	136	142	160	151	217	163	135	142	149	150

1. What is the mean of the scores? _____

2. What is the median of the scores? _____

3. What is the mode of the scores? _____

4. List any outliers that are in Bill's scores. _____

5. After Bill bowled his eleventh game, his mean score was 159. What was Bill's score in his eleventh game?

    _____

6. Nine out of ten students received these scores on a physics quiz.

    19, 16, 20, 19, 15, 19, 16, 14, 20

    If the median of all ten scores is 18, what score did the tenth student receive?

    _____

Directions: Use these numbers to answer Numbers 7 and 8.

358, 330, 344, 336, 358, 382, 343, 375, 336, 358

7. What is the mean?

    A. 351
    B. 352
    C. 358
    D. 370

8. What is the mode?

    A. 336
    B. 346
    C. 358
    D. 370

© 2002 Buckle Down Publishing Company. DO NOT DUPLICATE.

Uses of the Measures of Central Tendency

The measure of central tendency that is best to use in a given situation depends on the numbers in the data set and the purpose that the measure is to serve.

Example

Angie is setting sales goals for the Art Club fund-raiser. The club is selling posters and mugs to raise money for a trip to a museum. The following list shows the amounts raised by the 13 members of the club during last year's fund-raiser.

$10, $15, $20, $20, $20, $20, $25, $25, $30, $40, $46, $90, $120

mean: $37   median: $25   mode: $20

If Angie were to set goals based on this data set, what measures of central tendency are best to use?

If Angie wants to set goals based on the **average** amount raised during the last fund-raiser, it is best to use the **mean**, which was $37.

If she wants to set goals based on the **middle** amount raised during the last fund-raiser, it is best to use the **median**, which was $25.

If she wants to set goals based on what **most** members actually raised during the last fund-raiser, it is best to use the **mode**. The amount reported most often was $20.

Angie could use any of these measures in presenting goals to her group. The one she chooses will depend on what she wants to accomplish. She might choose the mode or median if she wants to be realistic about what members might actually be expected to sell. If she wants to encourage members to do more than might reasonably be expected (based on past sales), she might choose the mean.

The mean is usually not very accurate for interpreting the center of a data set that has outliers. In this example, $90 and $120 are outliers since they are much larger than the rest of the data values. Outliers can also be much smaller than the rest of the data values.

© 2002 Buckle Down Publishing Company. DO NOT DUPLICATE.

Practice

Directions: Use this information to answer Numbers 1 through 3.

Daniel is a biology student working on a lab experiment. He wrote these data values in his notebook: 3, 4, 5, 2, 3, 4, 4, 30, 2.

1. Find the mean, median, and mode of the data values. (Round to the nearest tenth if necessary.)

    mean: _____   median: _____   mode: _____

2. Daniel's lab partner saw the number 30 and decided that it was an outlier. He removed it from the data, which left the following: 3, 4, 5, 2, 3, 4, 4, 2. Find the mean, median, and mode of these data values. (Round to the nearest tenth if necessary.)

    mean: _____   median: _____   mode: _____

3. Compare the means, medians, and modes in Numbers 1 and 2. Which measure of central tendency gives the least accurate interpretation of the center of the data set that has an outlier? Explain.

    _____

    _____

Directions: Use the following information to answer Numbers 4 and 5.

The ages of six students who went on a geology field trip are 16, 15, 17, 14, 16, and 15. The age of the instructor who went with them is 28, and the age of the instructor's nephew who also went with them is 3.

4. Find the mean and the median of all the ages.

    mean: _____   median: _____

5. Explain why the mean is just as accurate as the median for describing the center of this data set, even though there are outliers in the data set.

    _____

    _____

© 2002 Buckle Down Publishing Company. DO NOT DUPLICATE.

Range

Range is the difference between the highest value and the lowest value in a data set. Range is a measure of variability. It shows how far apart the values of a data set are spread.

Example

These two lists show the number of items that two students answered incorrectly on six different tests.

Greg: 0, 10, 1, 5, 5, 9

Marsha: 4, 5, 5, 5, 6, 5

Find the ranges of Greg's and Marsha's data.

Greg's range: $10 - 0 = \mathbf{10}$

Marsha's range: $6 - 4 = \mathbf{2}$

While the mean, median, and mode are exactly the same for these two sets of data, the ranges, **10** and **2**, are very different. Greg's range indicates that his data values are more spread out than Marsha's.

Practice

Directions: Find the range of each set of numbers in Numbers 1 and 2.

1. 98, 78, 71, 62, 94, 86, 71, 81   range: _____

2. 52, 86, 54, 23, 79, 63, 28, 45   range: _____

3. If the range of a set of numbers is 62 and the smallest number in the set is 33, what is the largest number in the set?

   A. 29
   B. 62
   C. 91
   D. 95

4. If the range of a set of numbers is 49 and the largest number in the set is 31, what is the smallest number in the set?

   A. 80
   B. 18
   C. –18
   D. –31

© 2002 Buckle Down Publishing Company. DO NOT DUPLICATE.

Test Your Skills

Directions: Use the following table to answer Numbers 1 through 6.

Golf Scores

Tom	81	77	80	83	74	71	76	81	79
Matt	76	77	81	79	73	72	75	108	79

1. What is the mode of Matt's scores?

   A. 73
   B. 77
   C. 79
   D. 80

2. What is the range of Tom's scores?

   A. 2
   B. 9
   C. 12
   D. 36

3. Which statement is true?

   A. Tom's median score is 2 strokes higher than Matt's median score.
   B. Tom's median score is 2 strokes lower than Matt's median score.
   C. Tom's median score is 1 stroke higher than Matt's median score.
   D. Tom's median score is 1 stroke lower than Matt's median score.

4. What is the mode of Tom's scores?

   A. 78
   B. 79
   C. 80
   D. 81

5. How much higher is Matt's mean score than Tom's mean score?

   A. 1 stroke
   B. 2 strokes
   C. 3 strokes
   D. 4 strokes

6. Is the mean the **best** measure of central tendency to use to compare Tom's and Matt's golf scores? Explain.

© 2002 Buckle Down Publishing Company. DO NOT DUPLICATE.

Lesson 7: Displaying Data

Graphic displays of numerical data are useful for summarizing information, showing trends, making predictions, and drawing conclusions.

Frequency Charts

A **frequency chart** is used to show data values and the number of times each value occurs (the frequency).

Example

The following list shows the high temperatures (in degrees Fahrenheit) recorded in Lakeville for the month of June.

69, 60, 60, 61, 60, 63, 62, 65, 66, 62, 65, 60, 61, 64, 63, 69, 60, 62, 61, 62, 64, 65, 68, 62, 63, 68, 69, 60, 62, 62

This data is displayed in the following frequency chart. The numbers of tally marks, called the frequencies, are listed in the third column.

High Temperatures in June

Temperature (°F)	Tally Marks	Frequency
60	卌 I	6
61	III	3
62	卌 II	7
63	III	3
64	II	2
65	III	3
66	I	1
67		0
68	II	2
69	III	3

Notice that the temperatures are written in order from 60°F to 69°F. The temperature of 67°F was not recorded but is still shown in the chart with a frequency of zero.

© 2002 Buckle Down Publishing Company. DO NOT DUPLICATE.

TIP: A frequency chart is also known as a **frequency table**.

Practice

1. This list shows the number of miles that 30 students rode on a bike hike.

   2, 15, 14, 12, 6, 8, 9, 15, 6, 4, 12, 11, 6, 2, 8,
   15, 11, 10, 9, 7, 15, 1, 7, 14, 10, 5, 5, 8, 4, 9

   Fill in the frequency chart with the data.

   Bike Hike

Distance Traveled	Tally Marks	Frequency
1–5 miles		
6–10 miles		
11–15 miles		

Directions: Use the following information to answer Numbers 2 through 4.

This list shows the number of push-ups done by the students in Mr. Cooper's gym class.

   25, 29, 26, 30, 25, 29, 26, 27, 25, 25, 30, 30, 23, 29, 25, 26, 29

2. Fill in the following frequency chart with the data.

   Class Push-Ups

Number of Push-ups	Tally Marks	Frequency

3. What is the mean number of push-ups?

   A. 25
   B. 26
   C. 27
   D. 28

4. What is the median number of push-ups?

   A. 25
   B. 25.5
   C. 26
   D. 26.5

© 2002 Buckle Down Publishing Company. DO NOT DUPLICATE.

Bar Graphs

Data from a frequency chart can be displayed in a **bar graph**. A bar graph is a diagram that uses horizontal or vertical bars to show data.

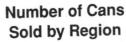

Example

The following frequency chart shows the sales of a new soft drink on a given day in each region of the United States. The numbers are rounded to the nearest thousand.

Number of Cans Sold by Region

Region	Number of Cans
Northeast (NE)	6,000
Southeast (SE)	9,000
West (W)	2,000
Midwest (MW)	4,000
Southwest (SW)	10,000

This is how the data look in a bar graph.

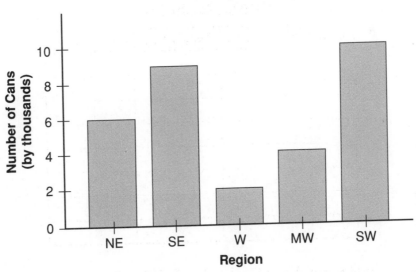

© 2002 Buckle Down Publishing Company. DO NOT DUPLICATE.

Practice

1. The following frequency chart shows the monthly precipitation that Stewart recorded last year in Minnesota.

Monthly Precipitation

Month	Precipitation (in inches)
January	4.28
February	2.59
March	1.97
April	4.19
May	2.27
June	2.07
July	3.81
August	3.15
September	1.94
October	2.17
November	2.60
December	2.58

Use the information from the chart to make a bar graph of the data.

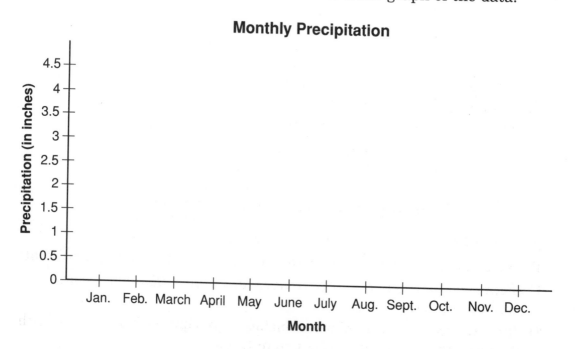

Monthly Precipitation

© 2002 Buckle Down Publishing Company. DO NOT DUPLICATE.

Directions: Use the frequency chart and the bar graph you created in Number 1 to answer Numbers 2 through 8.

2. What month had the **highest** amount of precipitation? _____

3. What month had the **lowest** amount of precipitation? _____

4. What is the median amount of precipitation that fell? _____

5. List the months that had the following amounts of precipitation.

   0–1 inches: _____

   1–2 inches: _____

   2–3 inches: _____

   3–4 inches: _____

   4–5 inches: _____

6. What is the total amount of precipitation for the entire year? _____

7. What four consecutive months had the lowest total amount of precipitation?

   A. March, April, May, June
   B. January, February, March, April
   C. July, August, September, October
   D. September, October, November, December

8. Which conclusion **cannot** be made from the bar graph?

   A. About twice as much precipitation fell in April as in June.
   B. No two consecutive months had more than three inches of precipitation.
   C. February, November, and December had approximately the same amount of precipitation.
   D. Two months had less than two inches of precipitation and two months had more than four inches of precipitation.

© 2002 Buckle Down Publishing Company. DO NOT DUPLICATE.

Histograms

Data from a frequency chart can be displayed in a bar graph called a **histogram**. A histogram has the following characteristics.

- There is no space between the bars.
- The bars are always vertical.
- Each bar has the same width.

Example

The following frequency chart shows math midterm scores for 40 students.

Math Midterm

Score	Frequency
61–65	2
66–70	3
71–75	5
76–80	8
81–85	9
86–90	7
91–95	4
96–100	2

This is how the data look in a histogram.

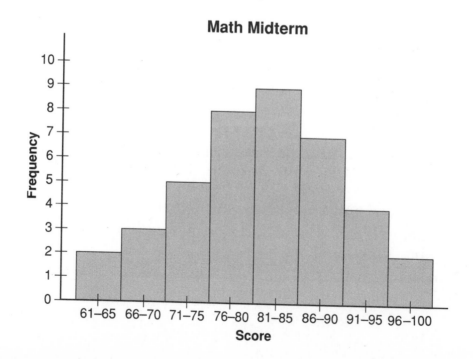

© 2002 Buckle Down Publishing Company. DO NOT DUPLICATE.

▷ **Practice**

1. The following frequency chart shows the heights (to the nearest inch) of all the students in the 10th-grade class at Harrison High School.

10th-Graders' Heights

Height	Frequency
51–55	12
56–60	38
61–65	79
66–70	89
71–75	60
76–80	18
81–85	4

Use the information from the frequency chart to make a histogram of the data.

10th-Graders' Heights

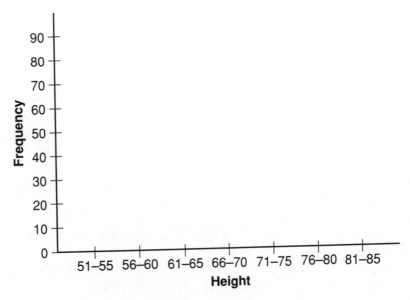

Directions: Use the frequency chart and the histogram you created in Number 1 to answer Numbers 2 through 9.

2. How many more students had heights in the 61–65 inch interval than in the 71–75 inch interval?

_____

3. How many students are 71 inches or taller? _____

4. How many students are in the 10th-grade class at Harrison High School?

_____

5. What height interval contains exactly 20% of the students? _____

6. What is the minimum number of students that can be taller than 6 feet?

_____

7. Explain why it is not possible to find the range of the heights.

_____

_____

_____

8. Which of the following is **not** possible for the number of students who had a height of 55 in.?

A. 0
B. 6
C. 12
D. 15

9. What interval contains the median height?

A. 56–60
B. 61–65
C. 66–70
D. 71–75

© 2002 Buckle Down Publishing Company. DO NOT DUPLICATE.

Line Graphs

Line graphs are useful for showing trends over a period of time. A **trend** is a clear direction in a graph that suggests how the data values will behave in the future. A line graph can have an increasing trend, a decreasing trend, or no trend at all.

Example

The following table shows the number of teams that have played in the National Basketball Association (NBA) since 1960, using 5-year increments.

NBA Teams

Year	1960	1965	1970	1975	1980	1985	1990	1995	2000
Number of Teams	8	9	14	18	22	23	27	29	29

While it is possible to see that there is an increasing trend by looking at the numbers alone, a line graph shows the information more clearly.

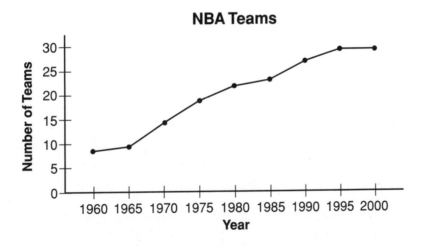

What inferences can be drawn from the graph? For example, what do you predict the number of teams will be in the year 2010? A reasonable prediction is that the number of teams will be greater than or equal to the last data value, which is 29. But can a more specific number be found? If so, how can you find that number?

© 2002 Buckle Down Publishing Company. DO NOT DUPLICATE.

To make a prediction for the year 2010, first extend the vertical and horizontal axes, then continue the trend by extending the line.

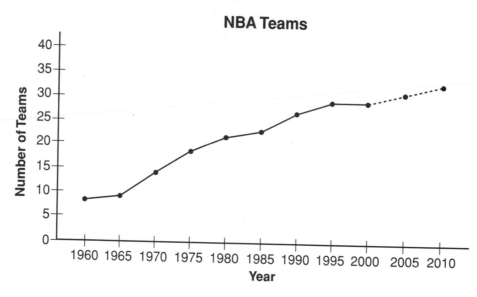

NBA Teams

The extended line shows that there will be about 32 teams in 2010, if the trend continues.

Practice

1. The following table shows Monica's savings account balance for six months.

Monica's Savings Account Balance

June	July	August	September	October	November
$300	$250	$350	$400	$325	$350

Use the information from the table to make a line graph of the data.

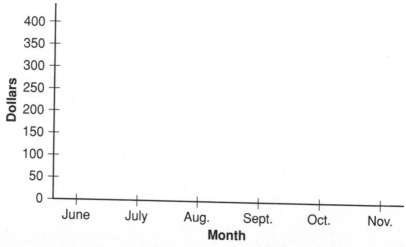

Monica's Savings Account Balance

© 2002 Buckle Down Publishing Company. DO NOT DUPLICATE.

Directions: Use the table and the line graph you created in Number 1 to answer Numbers 2 through 8.

2. In what month did Monica's savings account show the biggest **increase** over the previous month?

   _____

3. In what month did Monica's savings account show the biggest **decrease** over the previous month?

   _____

4. How much **more** did Monica have in her savings account in November than in June?

   _____

5. If the overall trend for the past six months continues, do you predict that Monica's savings account will increase or decrease over the next six months? Explain.

   _____

   _____

   _____

6. What is the range of the amount of money Monica had in her savings account for the past six months?

   _____

7. In which month did Monica have the most money in her savings account?

   A. July
   B. September
   C. October
   D. November

8. In which two months did Monica have the same amount in her savings account?

   A. July and September
   B. August and October
   C. August and November
   D. October and November

© 2002 Buckle Down Publishing Company. DO NOT DUPLICATE.

Circle Graphs

Circle graphs (sometimes called **pie charts**) are used to show how different parts of a whole compare to one another. Each part can be expressed as a fraction (the sum of all the parts adds up to 1) or as a percent (the sum of all the parts equals 100%).

A circle graph shows information at one particular time and does not show trends or changes over a period of time.

 Example

The following table shows the types of vegetables the Miller family sold at a farmer's market.

Millers' Vegetable Sales

Vegetable	Pounds Sold	Percent Sold
Carrots	522	33%
Cucumbers	285	18%
Yellow Squash	543	35%
Zucchini	216	14%
TOTAL	**1,566**	**100%**

Sometimes it is difficult to compare data at a glance when it is shown in a table. The same data, shown in a circle graph, is easier to compare.

Millers' Vegetable Sales

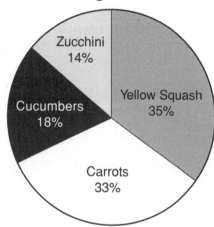

© 2002 Buckle Down Publishing Company. DO NOT DUPLICATE.

Practice

1. The Millers sold 50 pies at the farmer's market. They made the following table to keep track of their sales.

Millers' Pie Sales

Pie	Number Sold	Percent
Apple	24	48%
Cherry	13	26%
Blueberry	4	8%
Lemon	4	8%
Rhubarb	5	10%
TOTAL	**50**	**100%**

Use the information from the table to make a circle graph of the data.

Millers' Pie Sales

© 2002 Buckle Down Publishing Company. DO NOT DUPLICATE.

Directions: Use the table and the circle graph you created in Number 1 to answer Numbers 2 through 8.

2. What kind of pie did the Millers sell the most? _____

3. What two kinds of pies did the Millers sell the least?

    _____

4. What kind of pie represents about one-fourth of the pies sold?

    _____

5. How many more apple pies needed to be sold to make the apple pie section exactly half of the circle? (Base your answer on a total sale of 50 pies.)

    _____

6. What sections could you combine to make a section that is equal to the cherry pie section?

    _____

7. The Millers' goal is to double their pie sales next week. If they achieve their goal and the percent of each kind of pie sold stays the same, how many blueberry pies will they sell next week?

    A. 4
    B. 6
    C. 8
    D. 10

8. If the Millers sell an equal number of each kind of pie next week, what percent will show up in each section of the circle graph?

    A. 10%
    B. 20%
    C. 25%
    D. 50%

© 2002 Buckle Down Publishing Company. DO NOT DUPLICATE.

Box-and-Whisker Plots

A **box-and-whisker plot** is used to show how a large data set clusters together. It shows the median, the quartiles, and the minimum and maximum values. **Quartile** is a word used in statistics to represent one-fourth of the data set. The **lower quartile** is the median of the lower half; the **upper quartile** is the median of the upper half. The **minimum value** is the smallest value; the **maximum value** is the largest value.

Example

During the first 13 days of school, a store sold the following number of calculators.

8, 14, 24, 5, 8, 15, 3, 13, 9, 6, 5, 10, 23

The following diagram shows how to arrange and separate the data values.

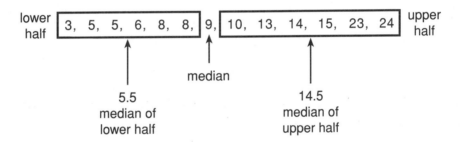

To construct a box-and-whisker plot, draw five points with the correct scale between them to represent the following.

minimum value: 3

lower quartile: 5.5

median: 9

upper quartile: 14.5

maximum value: 24

Now draw vertical lines through the points representing the lower quartile, median, and upper quartile and connect them to make a box around those points. Then draw horizontal lines from the outside of the box to connect the lower quartile to the minimum value and the upper quartile to the maximum value.

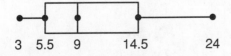

© 2002 Buckle Down Publishing Company. DO NOT DUPLICATE.

Practice

1. The following list shows the scores in the Tournament of Gutter-Ball Bowling Champions.

   57, 61, 58, 54, 68, 51, 49, 64, 50, 48, 65,
   52, 56, 46, 47, 55, 42, 60, 62, 43, 69

   Make a box-and-whisker plot of the data.

Directions: Use the box-and-whisker plot you made in Number 1 to answer Numbers 2 through 6.

2. What is the median of this data set? _____

3. What is the lower quartile of this data set? _____

4. What is the maximum value of this data set? _____

5. What is the upper quartile of this data set?

   A. 42

   B. 48.5

   C. 61.5

   D. 69

6. What is the minimum value of this data set?

   A. 42

   B. 48.5

   C. 55

   D. 61.5

© 2002 Buckle Down Publishing Company. DO NOT DUPLICATE.

Stem-and-Leaf Plots

A **stem-and-leaf plot** is used to find the maximum and minimum values of a data set, as well as the median and the mode. For a single-digit value, the stem is zero and the leaf is the number itself. For a two-digit value, the tens digit is the stem and the ones digit is the leaf. For a three-digit value, the hundreds and tens digits are the stem and the ones digit is the leaf. Holes in the data set occur when there are stems without any leaves. A hole in the data set is called an empty interval.

Example

The following list shows the number of fish caught by each of the 50 entrants in a three-day-long fishing tournament.

9, 52, 50, 94, 85, 75, 64, 12, 18, 29, 94, 51, 53, 19, 123, 101, 62, 93, 88, 67, 25, 74, 59, 60, 89, 129, 39, 75, 55, 56, 39, 99, 107, 62, 56, 73, 31, 112, 94, 85, 27, 34, 52, 76, 65, 55, 79, 100, 77, 22

This is how the data look in a stem-and-leaf plot.

Number of Fish Caught

```
 0 | 9
 1 | 2 8 9
 2 | 2 5 7 9
 3 | 1 4 9 9
 4 |
 5 | 0 1 2 2 3 5 5 6 6 9
 6 | 0 2 2 4 5 7
 7 | 3 4 5 5 6 7 9
 8 | 5 5 8 9
 9 | 3 4 4 4 9
10 | 0 1 7
11 | 2
12 | 3 9
```

After you record the information in a stem-and-leaf plot, you can find the minimum value, the maximum value, the median, the mode, and any holes that may exist.

For this data set, the minimum number of fish caught is 9, the maximum number is 129, the median is 63, the mode is 94, and a hole is the empty interval 40–49.

© 2002 Buckle Down Publishing Company. DO NOT DUPLICATE.

Practice

1. Mrs. McCormick, the 10th-grade physical education instructor, organized pulse rate data values for her first-period class. The students' pulse rates were taken after each student had completed one minute of running in place. Make a stem-and-leaf plot of the following data values.

    102, 180, 115, 122, 129, 175, 103, 135,
    144, 138, 129, 162, 129, 175, 145

Pulse Rates

```
10 |
11 |
12 |
13 |
14 |
15 |
16 |
17 |
18 |
```

Directions: Use the stem-and-leaf plot that you made in Number 1 to answer Numbers 2 through 6.

2. What is the median of the data set? _____

3. What is the mode of the data set? _____

4. Identify the empty interval. _____

5. What is the minimum value?

    A. 102
    B. 103
    C. 115
    D. 135

6. What is the maximum value?

    A. 135
    B. 145
    C. 175
    D. 180

© 2002 Buckle Down Publishing Company. DO NOT DUPLICATE.

Scatterplots

A **scatterplot** is used to show how two data sets are related. The data values are plotted as ordered pairs and then observed to see how closely they come to forming a straight line.

Example

The following table shows the number of hours Juanita studied for each of her first seven math tests and the grade she received on each test.

Grade Versus Study Time

Study Time (in hours)	1.5	3.0	1.0	2.5	1.5	3.5	4.0
Grade	80	90	70	88	85	95	98

This is how the data look in a scatterplot.

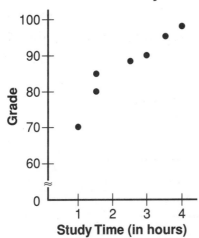

The scatterplot shows that the data points come close to forming a straight line. The more hours Juanita studied, the higher the grade she received on the test. This relationship is **direct:** as one quantity increases, the other quantity increases. Relationships can also be **inverse:** as one quantity increases, the other quantity decreases.

© 2002 Buckle Down Publishing Company. DO NOT DUPLICATE.

Correlation and trend lines

When two data sets are related, we say they are **correlated**. A direct relationship represents a **positive correlation**. An inverse relationship represents a **negative correlation**. The closer the data points come to forming a straight line, the more strongly they are correlated. When the data points lie in a straight line, the data sets are perfectly correlated. Two data sets that have no relationship have **no correlation**.

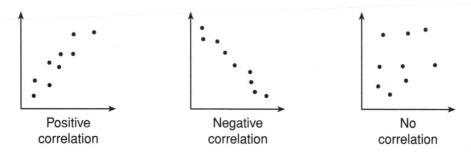

When data sets show a positive or negative correlation, a **trend line** can be drawn to approximate missing data. A trend line has close to the same number of data points above as below it.

 Example

Here is the scatterplot from the previous page with a trend line drawn through the data.

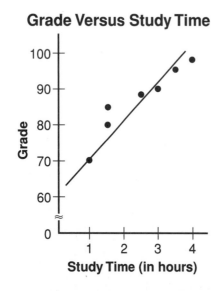

The scatterplot shows a positive correlation between study time and grade. The trend line has been drawn through the data points in order to make predictions about missing values. Looking at the trend line, it appears that if Juanita studies for 2 hours she will receive a grade of about 80. (This is a prediction, since the table does not include a study time of 2.0 hours.)

© 2002 Buckle Down Publishing Company. DO NOT DUPLICATE.

© 2002 Buckle Down Publishing Company. DO NOT DUPLICATE.

Practice

Directions: Write whether each scatterplot in Numbers 1 through 4 shows positive, negative, or no correlation. If the scatterplot shows positive or negative correlation, draw a trend line and make the given prediction.

1.

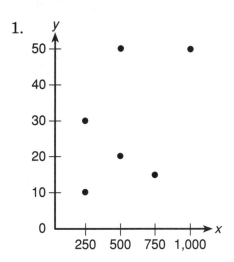

correlation: _____

prediction for y when x is 300: _____

2.

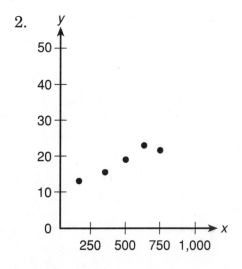

correlation: _____

prediction for y when x is 1,000: _____

3.

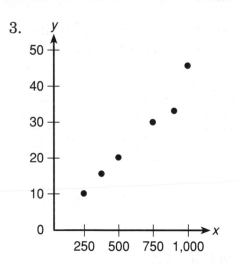

correlation: _____

prediction for y when x is 600: _____

4.

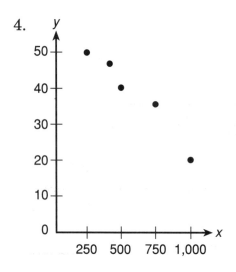

correlation: _____

prediction for y when x is 850: _____

© 2002 Buckle Down Publishing Company. DO NOT DUPLICATE.

5. The following table shows the number of hours of sleep a group of 10th-grade students got the night before a math test and each student's score.

Math Score Versus Hours of Sleep

Hours of Sleep	9	4	7	6	6	8	9	8	5	7	8	7
Math Test Score	93	71	84	77	82	93	91	100	70	83	90	90

Use the information from the table to make a scatterplot of the data. Then draw a trend line through the data.

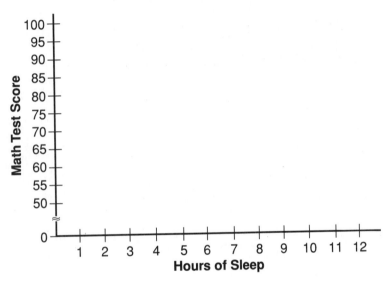

Math Score Versus Hours of Sleep

Directions: Use the scatterplot you created in Number 5 to answer Numbers 6 through 8.

6. Does the scatterplot show a positive or a negative correlation? _____

7. If a student got 2 hours of sleep, what is your prediction for his or her score?

_____

8. Which statement about the scatterplot is **true**?

A. It has a perfect correlation.

B. It has a strong correlation.

C. It has a weak correlation.

D. It has no correlation.

© 2002 Buckle Down Publishing Company. DO NOT DUPLICATE.

Which Visual is Best?

The format that you use to present your data depends on what you want to convey to your audience.

Visual Formats and Purposes

Format	Purpose of Data
table or chart	organizing numbers
bar graph	comparing amounts
histogram	comparing amounts
line graph	showing change over time
circle graph	comparing parts of a whole
box-and-whisker plot	showing how data are clustered
stem-and-leaf plot	showing how data are clustered
scatterplot	showing relationships between data

Practice

Directions: For each situation in Numbers 1 through 5, identify the best format to use to display the data being collected.

1. You want to know if there is a relationship between students' heights and their speeds in the 50-yard dash.

   _____

2. You want to show how sales of a new toy have risen or fallen over the last 12 months.

   _____

3. You want to compare the ticket sales of four movies for the first month they were shown in theaters.

   _____

4. You want to list the names of the frozen desserts for sale at your store along with each one's original price, sale price, and percent savings.

   _____

5. You want to show how the money earned by the school fund-raiser was divided to purchase several items for the school.

   _____

© 2002 Buckle Down Publishing Company. DO NOT DUPLICATE.

Misrepresentations of Data

You have seen that graphs can reveal patterns in data sets that are simple to see at a single glance. However, graphs can be manipulated so that the same information looks as if it is showing different things.

Example

The Smith family decided to hire a financial consultant to help them attract potential investors to their small business. After the Smiths provided the necessary data values, the consultant made the following two line graphs to use in his presentation.

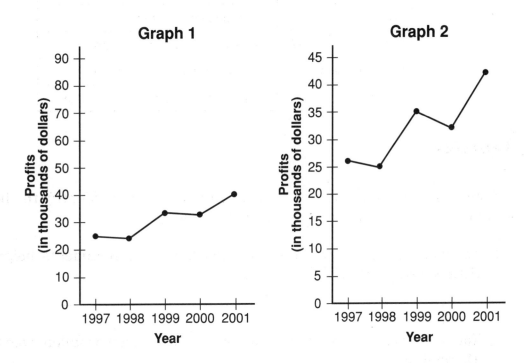

The consultant stated that Graph 1 shows a slight increase in profits, while Graph 2 shows a more rapid growth in profits. The consultant also stated that Graph 2 would be better to use in his presentation since it shows a stronger trend toward overall growth.

Do both of these graphs use the same data values? If so, why do they look so different? Use the graphs to find the answers to these and other questions in the practice exercises on the following page.

TIP: A **scale interval** is the difference between two consecutive values on an axis.

© 2002 Buckle Down Publishing Company. DO NOT DUPLICATE.

Practice

Directions: Use the example on page 145 to answer Numbers 1 through 6.

1. What are the least and greatest values on the vertical axis on Graph 1?

   least _____   greatest _____

2. What are the least and greatest values on the vertical axis on Graph 2?

   least _____   greatest _____

3. What is the scale interval on the vertical axis used on Graph 1? _____

4. What is the scale interval on the vertical axis used on Graph 2? _____

5. If the consultant's audience looks only at Graph 1 and does not carefully read the numbers on the vertical axis, what might be the interpretation?

   _____

   _____

   _____

6. If the consultant's audience looks only at Graph 2 and does not carefully read the numbers on the vertical axis, what might be the interpretation?

   _____

   _____

   _____

© 2002 Buckle Down Publishing Company. DO NOT DUPLICATE.

Test Your Skills

1. For the month of October, Video Palace determined that 33% of its rentals were comedies, 25% were action movies, 25% were dramas, and 17% were all other types of movies. Which circle graph displays the data correctly?

A.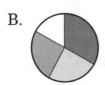

B.

C.

D.

2. Dan wants to know if there is a relationship between the number of hours he practices football each week and the percentage of passes he completes in each game. Which format is the best to use to display the data?

A. bar graph

B. line graph

C. scatterplot

D. stem-and-leaf plot

3. Which stem-and-leaf plot represents the following data?

39, 25, 41, 39, 23, 43, 39, 42, 24, 33

A.
Stem	Leaf
2	1 1 1
3	1 1 1
4	1 1 1

B.
Stem	Leaf
2	23 24 25
3	33 39 39 39
4	41 42 43

C.
Stem	Leaf
2	3
3	4
4	5

D.
Stem	Leaf
2	3 4 5
3	3 9 9 9
4	1 2 3

4. What is the upper quartile of the following box-and-whisker plot?

5   8   10   17   25

A. 5

B. 8

C. 10

D. 17

© 2002 Buckle Down Publishing Company. DO NOT DUPLICATE.

Directions: Use the following line graph to answer Numbers 5 and 6.

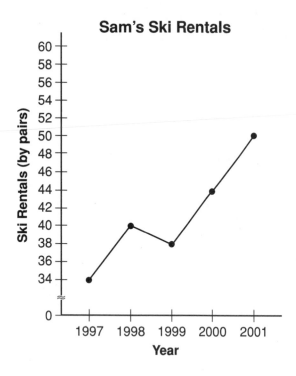

5. If the recent trend of these data values continues, predict the number of pairs of skis Sam will rent in 2002.

   A. 56

   B. 52

   C. 50

   D. 48

6. How many more pairs of skis did Sam rent in 2001 than in 1997?

   A. 6

   B. 16

   C. 34

   D. 84

7. Which graph shows overall growth in sales for Gene's Jeans Company?

   A.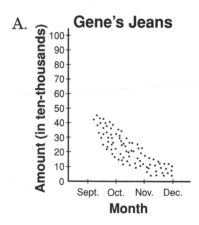

   B.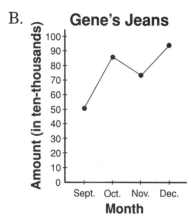

   C.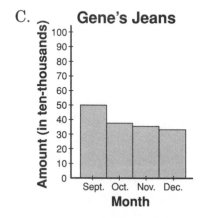

   D.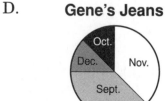

© 2002 Buckle Down Publishing Company. DO NOT DUPLICATE.

8. Ricky made the following graph to represent the number of stolen bases in Major League Baseball in 2000 and 2001.

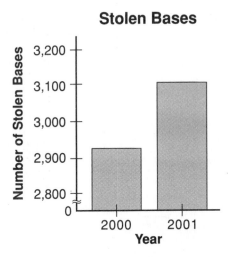

Ricky concluded that there were about twice as many stolen bases in Major League Baseball in 2001 than in 2000. In the space provided below, determine whether his conclusion is reasonable. Support your answer by showing your work or providing an explanation.

© 2002 Buckle Down Publishing Company. DO NOT DUPLICATE.

9. The following bar graph shows the number of school dances that were held each month for the entire school year.

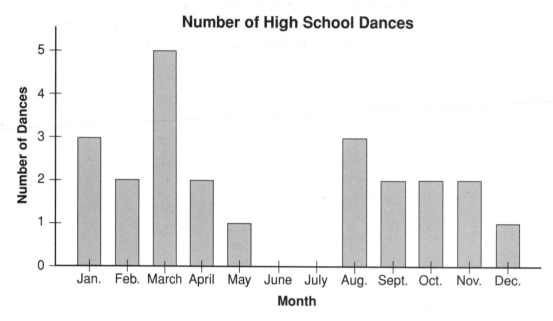

Number of High School Dances

During which month was the greatest number of dances held?

A. March

B. October

C. January

D. December

10. The following scatterplot shows the relationship between x and y.

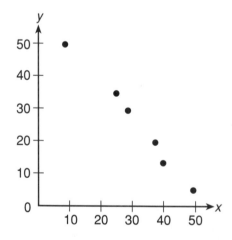

Based on the scatterplot, what is the best prediction for y when x is 15?

A. 35

B. 40

C. 45

D. 50

© 2002 Buckle Down Publishing Company. DO NOT DUPLICATE.

11. The highest scoring average for the twelve members of a basketball team is 16.2 points per game. The range is 13.7, the median is 5.2, and the mode is 4.5. In the space provided below, create a list of possible scoring averages for each player based on the information given. Create a box-and-whisker plot to display your data set. Find the mean of your data set.

© 2002 Buckle Down Publishing Company. DO NOT DUPLICATE.

Lesson 8: Probability

Probability (P), where $0 \le P \le 1$, is a measure of the likelihood that an event (E) will occur. The probability of an event is the ratio of the number of outcomes of the event to the total number of outcomes. Different counting techniques can be used to determine the total number of outcomes of an event. When finding the probability of choosing a certain item from some type of container in this lesson, assume all trials are done without looking.

Sample Space

A **sample space (S)** is the set { } of all possible outcomes. Duplicate outcomes are omitted.

Example

Christy's school is planning a carnival. They will choose one of the four seasons as a theme. What is the sample space?

The sample space consists of the 4 seasons.

$S = $ {spring, summer, fall, winter}

Example

The names of the 50 states of the union are put into a hat. A state is drawn at random and the first letter of the state's name is noted. What is the sample space?

The sample space consists of the first letters of the states' names. There are 19 outcomes. (Duplicate letters are omitted.)

$S = $ {A, C, D, F, G, H, I, K, L, M, N, O, P, R, S, T, U, V, W}

Practice

Directions: For Numbers 1 through 3, write the sample space.

1. A coin is flipped: $S = $ _____

2. The days of the week that start with T: $S = $ _____

3. The prime numbers less than 25: $S = $ _____

© 2002 Buckle Down Publishing Company. DO NOT DUPLICATE.

Counting techniques

There are two types of counting techniques that you will use to solve probability problems. The first technique involves listing all the outcomes of a situation. The second technique involves multiplication. If a complete list of every outcome is not needed, you can use multiplication to determine the total number of outcomes.

Tree diagrams

Tree diagrams are used to show the outcome set of a situation.

 Example

At Washington High School, a student is assigned to a gym class based on the following information.

Day: Tuesday (Tue.) or Thursday (Thurs.)

Time: A.M. or P.M.

Place: Gym 1 or Gym 2

The following tree diagram shows that there are 8 total outcomes for a gym class.

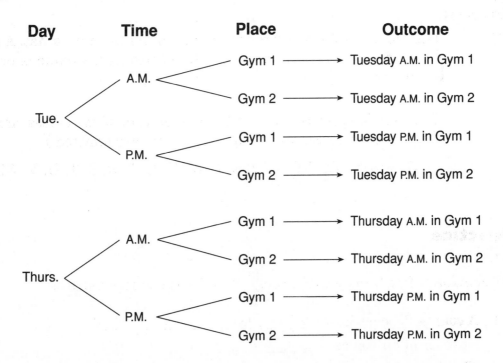

© 2002 Buckle Down Publishing Company. DO NOT DUPLICATE.

Practice

1. The first three questions on a history test are true/false. Make a tree diagram to show how many different ways the three questions can be answered. (Use T for true and F for false.)

   Number of outcomes: _____

2. A particular brand of shirt comes in two colors (white, gray), two sleeve lengths (long-sleeved, short-sleeved), and four sizes (S, M, L, XL). Make a tree diagram to show how many different types of this shirt are made.

   Number of outcomes: _____

© 2002 Buckle Down Publishing Company. DO NOT DUPLICATE.

3. A coin is tossed up in the air four times. Make a tree diagram to show how many different ways all four tosses can land. (Use H for heads and T for tails.)

Number of outcomes: _____

4. A meal at a certain restaurant includes one type each of meat, potato, and vegetable. The choices for meat are beef or chicken. The choices for potato are baked potato, hash browns, or french fries. The choices for vegetable are beans or carrots. Make a tree diagram to show how many different meals there are to choose from.

Number of outcomes: _____

© 2002 Buckle Down Publishing Company. DO NOT DUPLICATE.

Fundamental Counting Principle

The **Fundamental Counting Principle** is used to find the total number of outcomes when the possibilities are based on several separate parts. Multiply the number of ways that each part can be done to get the total number of outcomes.

Example

Al is going to order a one-topping pizza. He can choose from 4 sizes, 11 toppings, and 3 crust types. From how many different pizzas can Al choose?

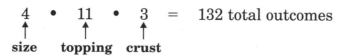

4 • 11 • 3 = 132 total outcomes

size   topping   crust

Al has 132 different pizzas to choose from.

Practice

Directions: For Numbers 1 through 4, use the Fundamental Counting Principle.

1. Using the digits 0–9, how many different four-digit numbers are possible? (Repetition of digits is allowed.)

   _____

2. The Spanish Club has 11 girls, 6 boys, and 3 adult chaperones going on a field trip. How many different groups of 1 girl, 1 boy, and 1 chaperone are there?

   _____

3. In several states, license plates consist of 3 digits followed by 3 letters. How many different license plates are possible? (Repetition of digits and letters is allowed.)

   _____

4. You are taking a 10-question true/false test and don't know any of the answers. You decide to guess on every question. How many different ways are there to mark your answer sheet?

   _____

© 2002 Buckle Down Publishing Company. DO NOT DUPLICATE.

Experimental Probability

Experimental probability is the probability of an event (E) based on an actual experiment. To find the experimental probability of an event, Exp $P(E)$, use the following formula.

$$\text{Exp } P(E) = \frac{\text{number of actual outcomes of the event}}{\text{number of trials in the experiment}}$$

Example

This table shows the outcomes from an experiment in which two different coins were tossed 10 times each.

Toss	1	2	3	4	5	6	7	8	9	10
Outcome	HT	HH	TT	TH	HT	TH	TH	HT	HT	TH

What is the experimental probability of HT?

Step 1: Find the number of actual outcomes of the event.

In the coin toss experiment, HT occurred 4 times.

Step 2: Find the number of trials in the experiment.

There are 10 trials in the experiment.

Step 3: Substitute the information into the formula.

$$\text{Exp } P(\text{HT}) = \frac{4}{10} = \frac{2}{5} \text{ (in lowest terms)}$$

The experimental probability of HT is $\frac{2}{5}$.

© 2002 Buckle Down Publishing Company. DO NOT DUPLICATE.

Directions: Use the following information to answer Numbers 1 through 8.

Henry has a spinner that is divided into five equal sections—blue, green, orange, red, and yellow. He spun the spinner for a number of times and recorded his results in the following table.

Color	Blue	Green	Orange	Red	Yellow
Frequency	5	9	7	9	0

1. How many trials were performed in this experiment? _____

2. Find Exp P(blue). _____

3. Find Exp P(green). _____

4. Find Exp P(orange). _____

5. Find Exp P(red). _____

6. Find Exp P(yellow). _____

7. Based on this experiment, if Henry spins the spinner 150 times, how many times can he expect the spinner to land on a blue section?

   A. 20
   B. 25
   C. 30
   D. 50

8. Based on this experiment, how many times do you think it would take for the spinner to land on the red section 12 times?

   A. 34
   B. 37
   C. 40
   D. 43

© 2002 Buckle Down Publishing Company. DO NOT DUPLICATE.

Theoretical Probability

Theoretical probability is used when an observation is not based on an actual experiment. In other words, you will infer, predict, or guess what will happen. A **probability of 0** means that the event **will not** occur. A **probability of 1** means that the event is **certain** to occur.

The difference between experimental probability and theoretical probability is that with experimental probability, you actually record all the outcomes. The greater the number of trials related to an experimental probability, the closer the outcomes will most likely be to the theoretical probability.

To find the theoretical probability of an event, use the following formula.

$$P(E) = \frac{\text{number of successful outcomes}}{\text{number of total outcomes}}$$

Example

A number cube numbered 1 through 6 is rolled. What is the theoretical probability that the number 3 will show on the top side?

Step 1: Find the number of successful outcomes.

There is 1 successful outcome. (3)

Step 2: Find the number of total outcomes.

There are 6 total outcomes. (1, 2, 3, 4, 5, 6)

Step 3: Substitute the information into the formula.

$$P(3) = \frac{1}{6}$$

The theoretical probability of the number 3 showing on the top of the number cube is $\frac{1}{6}$.

© 2002 Buckle Down Publishing Company. DO NOT DUPLICATE.

Practice

Directions: Use the following information to answer Numbers 1 through 3.

Walter wrote the names of the months of the year on identical slips of paper and put them into a box. If he picks out one slip, find the following probabilities.

1. *P*(picking a month that has exactly 4 letters) _____

2. *P*(picking a month that begins with a vowel) _____

3. *P*(picking a month that has at least 3 letters) _____

Directions: Use the following information to answer Numbers 4 through 6.

The following table shows the number of each color marble in a bag.

Color	Blue	Green	Orange	Red
Number	8	15	5	12

If Kristi picks a marble out of the bag, find the following probabilities.

4. *P*(picking a green marble) _____

5. *P*(picking a purple marble) _____

6. *P*(picking a blue marble) _____

7. Which of the following does not appear to be a theoretical probability?

   A. The probability that a coin will land heads up is $\frac{1}{2}$.

   B. The probability that a basketball player makes his or her next shot is $\frac{2}{3}$.

   C. The probability that you will roll a 7 on a cube numbered 1 through 6 is 0.

   D. The probability that your teacher's middle name starts with a vowel is $\frac{5}{26}$.

© 2002 Buckle Down Publishing Company. DO NOT DUPLICATE.

Complement of an Event

A **complement** of an event is the event that consists of all the outcomes in the sample space not associated with the given event. The complement is denoted by the symbol ′ next to the event (read as "not"). The sum of the probability of an event and its complement is always 1.

Example

If you roll a number cube numbered 1 through 6, what is $P(3')$?

There are 5 successful outcomes: 1, 2, 4, 5, 6.

There are still 6 total outcomes: 1, 2, 3, 4, 5, 6.

Substitute the information into the formula on page 159.

$$P(3') = \frac{5}{6}$$

The theoretical probability of **not 3** showing on top of the cube is $\frac{5}{6}$.

Practice

Directions: Use the following information to answer Numbers 1 through 3.

The following 10 students are trying out for the lead part in a school play: Maria, Linda, Holly, Brandy, Michelle, Lori, Haley, Tamika, Molly, and Carrie. The director put the names of all 10 students into a hat and will draw one to see who will read first for the lead part. Find the following probabilities.

1. $P(L)$ (drawing a name that starts with L) _____

2. $P(M')$ _____

3. $P(C)$ _____

4. If the probability of an event occurring is $\frac{3}{8}$, what is the probability of the event not occurring?

   _____

© 2002 Buckle Down Publishing Company. DO NOT DUPLICATE.

Independent and Dependent Events

Independent events are events that have no influence on each other. To find the probability of independent events occurring, multiply the probabilities of the individual events.

Example

There are 12 marbles in a coffee can: 5 are purple, 4 are blue, and 3 are red. What is the probability of taking a purple marble out of the can, replacing it, and then taking a red marble out of the can?

Does choosing the first marble have any effect on choosing the second marble? No. Since the first marble is replaced, the total number of marbles in the can is the same for each drawing.

P(purple marble first): $\frac{5}{12}$ $\qquad$ P(red marble second): $\frac{3}{12}$

P(purple marble first and red marble second): $\frac{5}{12} \cdot \frac{3}{12} = \frac{15}{144} = \frac{5}{48}$

The probability of taking a purple marble out first **and** a red marble out second **with** replacement is $\frac{5}{48}$.

Dependent events are events that are influenced by other events. To find the probability of dependent events occurring, multiply the probabilities of the individual events.

Example

Using the same coffee can of marbles as in the previous example, what is the probability of taking a purple marble out of the can, leaving it out, and then taking a red marble out of the can?

Does choosing the first marble have any effect on choosing the second marble? Yes. When you take the first marble out of the can without replacing it, the total number of marbles left is reduced by 1.

P(purple marble first): $\frac{5}{12}$ $\qquad$ P(red marble second): $\frac{3}{11}$

P(purple marble first and red marble second): $\frac{5}{12} \cdot \frac{3}{11} = \frac{15}{132} = \frac{5}{44}$

The probability of taking a purple marble out first **and** a red marble out second **without** replacement is $\frac{5}{44}$.

© 2002 Buckle Down Publishing Company. DO NOT DUPLICATE.

© 2002 Buckle Down Publishing Company. DO NOT DUPLICATE.

Practice

Directions: For Numbers 1 and 2, write whether the events are *independent* or *dependent*. Then find the probability of the event.

1. There are five questions on a true/false test. What is the probability that someone who guesses on every question will get them all correct?

_____

2. There are five questions on a matching test (exactly one answer is paired with one question). What is the probability that someone who guesses on all five questions will get them all correct?

_____

Directions: Use the following information to answer Numbers 3 through 5.

Mike has a drawerful of push-pins: 23 are white, 10 are yellow, 5 are orange, and 2 are red.

3. What is the probability of Mike taking a white push-pin from the drawer and then taking an orange push-pin from the drawer **with** replacement?

_____

4. What is the probability of Mike taking a yellow push-pin from the drawer and then taking a red push-pin from the drawer **without** replacement?

_____

5. Which expression shows the probability of Mike taking two white push-pins in a row from the drawer **without** replacement?

A. $\frac{23}{40} \cdot \frac{23}{40}$

B. $\frac{23}{40} \cdot \frac{22}{40}$

C. $\frac{23}{40} \cdot \frac{23}{39}$

D. $\frac{23}{40} \cdot \frac{22}{39}$

Mutually Exclusive Events

Mutually exclusive events are two or more events that cannot happen at the same time. To find the probability of mutually exclusive events occurring, add the probabilities of the individual events.

Example

Jason wears a dress shirt to work every day. He has 4 white dress shirts, 5 blue dress shirts, and 2 pinstriped dress shirts in his closet. If Jason takes one dress shirt out of his closet, what is the probability that it will be white or pinstriped?

$$P(\text{white}) = \frac{4}{11} \qquad\qquad P(\text{pinstriped}) = \frac{2}{11}$$

$$P(\text{white or pinstriped}) = \frac{4}{11} + \frac{2}{11} = \frac{6}{11}$$

The probability that Jason will take a white or pinstriped dress shirt out of his closet is $\frac{6}{11}$.

Practice

Directions: Use the following information to answer Numbers 1 through 5.

Liz has 25 pairs of socks in her drawer: 6 white, 2 black, 4 red, 5 purple, and 8 blue. If she takes a pair of socks out of her drawer, find the following probabilities.

1. $P(\text{red } \mathbf{or} \text{ blue})$ _____

2. $P(\text{black } \mathbf{or} \text{ purple})$ _____

3. $P(\text{blue } \mathbf{or} \text{ gray})$ _____

4. $P(\text{white, red, } \mathbf{or} \text{ blue})$ _____

5. $P(\text{white, black, red, purple, } \mathbf{or} \text{ blue})$ _____

© 2002 Buckle Down Publishing Company. DO NOT DUPLICATE.

Test Your Skills

1. Sandy has 10 chocolate chip cookies and 6 butterscotch chip cookies in her cookie jar. If she takes two cookies out of her cookie jar **without** replacement, what is the probability that both will be chocolate chip?

   A. $\frac{45}{128}$

   B. $\frac{25}{64}$

   C. $\frac{3}{8}$

   D. $\frac{1}{2}$

2. Jeff has a coin with heads on one side and tails on the other. If he flips it into the air, what is the probability that the coin will land either heads up **or** tails up?

   A. 0

   B. $\frac{1}{2}$

   C. 1

   D. 2

3. How many different 5-digit numbers can be created using the **odd** digits from 1 through 9? (Repetition of digits is allowed.)

   A. 120

   B. 945

   C. 2,500

   D. 3,125

Directions: Use the following information to answer Numbers 4 and 5.

A coin is tossed once, and a four-color spinner is spun once.

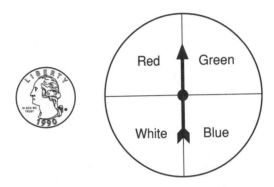

4. What is the probability that the coin will show tails **and** the spinner will **not** point to green?

   A. $\frac{1}{8}$

   B. $\frac{1}{4}$

   C. $\frac{3}{8}$

   D. $\frac{1}{2}$

5. What is the probability of getting heads **and** purple?

   A. 0

   B. $\frac{1}{8}$

   C. $\frac{3}{8}$

   D. $\frac{3}{4}$

© 2002 Buckle Down Publishing Company. DO NOT DUPLICATE.

6. Prizes in the Spirit Club raffle will be chosen by drawing tickets. First prize will be drawn first and second prize will be drawn second. There are 15 tickets. Sarah bought two tickets. What is the probability that she will win both the first and second prizes?

   A. $\frac{2}{59}$

   B. $\frac{2}{15}$

   C. $\frac{2}{30}$

   D. $\frac{1}{105}$

7. What is the sample space that consists of the perfect squares less than 40?

   A. {1, 4, 9, 16, 25, 36}
   B. {1, 2, 4, 8, 16, 32}
   C. {1, 2, 3, 4, 5, 6}
   D. {1, 8, 27}

8. An airline has seven morning flights from Columbus to Chicago and six afternoon flights from Chicago to Phoenix. How many different ways can a person fly on this airline from Columbus to Phoenix?

   A. 13
   B. 21
   C. 42
   D. 52

Directions: Use the following information to answer Numbers 9 and 10.

Eddie and Alice go to a snack bar at the beach. The snack bar sells the following items.

Sandwich	Drink	Side Order
hamburger	water	french fries
bratwurst	soda	onion rings
hot dog	juice	

9. If a meal from the snack bar consists of 1 sandwich, 1 drink, and 1 side order, how many different meals are possible?

   A. 6
   B. 8
   C. 9
   D. 18

10. Alice knows what kind of sandwich, drink, and side order she wants. Eddie wants to guess what she will order. What is the theoretical probability that he will guess correctly?

   A. $\frac{1}{6}$

   B. $\frac{1}{18}$

   C. $\frac{3}{8}$

   D. $\frac{1}{24}$

© 2002 Buckle Down Publishing Company. DO NOT DUPLICATE.

11. Doug's golf bag contains 3 yellow golf balls, 2 orange golf balls, 4 white golf balls, and 1 pink golf ball. Without looking, he took one ball out of his bag to use on his first tee shot. He hit the ball into the woods, so he took another ball out of his bag without looking. What is the probability that the first ball Doug took out of his bag was orange and the second ball was white?

A. $\frac{2}{25}$

B. $\frac{4}{45}$

C. $\frac{1}{5}$

D. $\frac{6}{20}$

12. Each patient at Dr. Wellness's office is classified according to his or her blood type (A, B, AB, or O) and blood pressure (high, normal, or low). In the space provided below, draw a tree diagram to show the number of ways a patient can be classified.

© 2002 Buckle Down Publishing Company. DO NOT DUPLICATE.

Appendix

© 2002 Buckle Down Publishing Company. DO NOT DUPLICATE.

Buckle Down Learning
Standards and Skills for
Algebra I, Book 2

Buckle Down Learning Standards and Skills for Algebra I, Book 2

Buckle Down on Algebra I, Book 2, is based on learning standards and skills common to mathematics curricula in the United States for Algebra I in the areas of Analytical Thinking and Data and Probability. The workbook teaches problem-solving and test-taking strategies that are generalizable to any test. The following table matches the standards and skills with the workbook lessons in which they are addressed.

Learning Standards and Skills	Buckle Down Lesson(s)
Standard 3: Analytical Thinking **The student will compute with polynomials, simplify and compute with rational expressions, extend patterns, find terms of sequences, evaluate series, and compute with matrices.**	
Skill 3.1 Add, subtract, multiply, and divide monomials.	1
Skill 3.2 Simplify monomials raised to a power.	1
Skill 3.3 Simplify monomials with negative exponents.	1
Skill 3.4 Simplify the square root and cube root of monomials.	1
Skill 3.5 Add, subtract, multiply, and divide polynomials.	1
Skill 3.6 Solve problems taken from real-world contexts using polynomials.	1
Skill 3.7 Find the greatest common factor of two or more monomials.	2
Skill 3.8 Factor the greatest common factor from polynomials.	2
Skill 3.9 Factor trinomials in the form $x^2 \pm bx \pm c$.	2
Skill 3.10 Factor trinomials in the form $ax^2 \pm bx \pm c$.	2
Skill 3.11 Factor binomials in the form $a^2 - c^2$.	2
Skill 3.12 Completely factor any binomial or trinomial.	2
Skill 3.13 Solve quadratic equations using factoring and the zero-product property.	2
Skill 3.14 Solve problems taken from real-world contexts using factoring and the zero-product property.	2
Skill 3.15 Find the least common denominator of two rational expressions.	3
Skill 3.16 Simplify, add, subtract, multiply, and divide rational expressions.	3
Skill 3.17 Find the rule for and extend number patterns.	4
Skill 3.18 Use the recursive and explicit definitions of both arithmetic and geometric sequences.	4

© 2002 Buckle Down Publishing Company. DO NOT DUPLICATE.

Learning Standards and Skills	*Buckle Down* Lesson(s)
Standard 3: **Analytical Thinking** *(Continued)*	
Skill 3.19 Solve problems taken from real-world contexts using arithmetic and geometric sequences.	4
Skill 3.20 Evaluate both arithmetic and geometric series.	4
Skill 3.21 Solve problems taken from real-world contexts using arithmetic and geometric series.	4
Skill 3.22 Solve problems taken from real-world contexts using patterns to make predictions and decisions.	4
Skill 3.23 Add and subtract matrices.	5
Skill 3.24 Multiply matrices by a scalar.	5
Skill 3.25 Solve problems taken from real-world contexts using addition, subtraction, and scalar multiplication of matrices.	5
Standard 4: **Data and Probability** **The student will find the measures of central tendency and range of data sets, display and interpret data sets using various representations, and find the probability that an event will occur.**	
Skill 4.1 Find the measures of central tendency of data sets.	6, 7
Skill 4.2 Find the range of data sets.	6, 7
Skill 4.3 Select, display, and interpret appropriate representations of data sets using a variety of charts, graphs, and plots.	7
Skill 4.4 Draw trend lines on plots to make predictions or to determine whether correlations exist in two-variable data sets.	7
Skill 4.5 Determine the number of outcomes and the sample space of probability situations.	8
Skill 4.6 Determine the experimental probabilities of events.	8
Skill 4.7 Determine the theoretical probabilities of events.	8
Skill 4.8 Determine the probabilities of the complements of events.	8
Skill 4.9 Determine the probabilities of dependent and independent events.	8
Skill 4.10 Determine the probabilities of mutually exclusive events.	8

© 2002 Buckle Down Publishing Company. DO NOT DUPLICATE.